PRIESTHOOD IN ACTION

AARONIC PRIESTHOOD STORIES FROM THE *NEW ERA*

THE NEW ERA

PRIESTHOOD IN
ACTION

AARONIC PRIESTHOOD STORIES FROM THE *NEW ERA*

THE NEW ERA ■ SALT LAKE CITY, UTAH

Library of Congress Catalog Card Number: 86-62151

THE NEW ERA

CONTENTS

PREFACE

For a young man in the Church, receiving the Aaronic Priesthood is a momentous occasion. As he advances from deacon to teacher to priest, more opportunities and responsibilities are opened to him. He learns step by step about the significance of the power he holds.

Holding the Aaronic Priesthood, or preparatory priesthood, helps young men understand that priesthood power is used to bless others. Young men learn while they are in their teens to prepare for missions and for future leadership in wards and stakes.

This book, *Priesthood in Action*, is a compilation of some of the best articles and stories printed in the *New Era* about the Aaronic Priesthood and experiences of young men with the priesthood in their lives. The topics range from the words of the prophet, doctrinal essays by General Authorities, and discussions of specific duties of deacons, teachers, and priests, to inspiring personal experiences by and about young men and good fiction that emphasizes the principles young Aaronic Priesthood holders should live by.

Just as these authors share their feelings and experiences, young Aaronic Priesthood holders continue to add to their knowledge of what the preparatory priesthood means and how it affects their decisions and actions.

AARONIC PRIEST- HOOD

TO
"THE RISING
GENERATION"

President Ezra Taft Benson

I pray for the inspiration of heaven as I direct my brief remarks to the youth of the Church—"the rising generation," as the Book of Mormon calls you (see Alma 5:49).

I want to talk to you young people frankly and honestly. I presume you know that we love you. As leaders of the Church, there isn't anything in this world that is right for you that we wouldn't do. We have great confidence in you. You are not just ordinary young men and women. You are choice spirits, many of you having been held in reserve for almost 6,000 years to come forth in this day, at this time, when the temptations, responsibilities, and opportunities are the very greatest.

God loves you as He loves each and every one of His children, and His desire and purpose and glory is to have you return to Him pure and undefiled, having proven yourselves worthy of an eternity in His presence.

Your Father in Heaven is mindful of you. He has given you commandments to guide you, to discipline you. He has also given you your agency—freedom of choice—"to see if [you] will do all things whatsoever [He] shall command" (Abr. 3:25). Freedom of choice is a God-given, eternal principle. His kingdom here on earth is well organized, and your leaders are dedicated to helping you. May you know that you have our constant love, our concern and prayers.

Satan is also mindful of you. He is committed to your destruction. He does not discipline you with commandments but offers instead a freedom to "do your own thing"—the freedom to smoke, to drink, to misuse drugs or rebel against the counsel and commandments of God and His servants. Satan knows that you are young, at the peak of physical vigor, excited by the world and consumed by new emotions.

Satan knows that youth is the springtime of life when all things are new and young people are most vulnerable. Youth is the spirit of adventure and awakening. It is a time of physical emerging when the body attains the vigor and good health that may ignore the caution of temperance. Youth is a period of timelessness when the horizons of age seem too distant to be noticed. Thus, the now generation forgets that the present will soon be the past, which one will look back upon either with sorrow and regret or joy and remembrance of cherished experiences. Satan's program is "play now and pay later." He seeks for all to be miserable like unto himself (see 2 Ne. 2:27). The Lord's program is happiness now and joy forever through gospel living. As one of His servants—and out of the love of my heart for the youth of Zion—I offer this counsel for your happiness now:

First, I counsel you to live a morally clean life. The prophet Alma declared—and truer words were never spoken—"Wickedness never was happiness" (Alma 41:10).

You cannot do wrong and feel right. It is impossible! Years of happiness can be lost in the foolish gratification of a momentary desire for pleasure. Satan would have you believe that happiness comes only as you surrender to his enticements, but one only needs to look at the shattered lives of those who violate God's laws to know why Satan is called the "Father of Lies."

Consider this letter from one young woman who said:

"I'm writing this from the depths of a broken heart, in the hope that it may be a warning to other girls never to partake of the bitterness that has come to me. I would give all that I have or ever hope to have if I could go back to those happy, carefree days before the first little taint of sin came upon my heart. I scarcely realized I was slipping into something that could bring such sorrow and ruin into a person's life.

"I wish I could reveal to you the anguish and regret that fill my heart today, the loss of self-respect and the realization that life's most priceless gift has slipped away from me. I reached out too eagerly for the excitements and thrills of life, and they have turned to ashes in my hands."

This young woman, unfortunately, discovered that the heaviest burden one may have to bear in this life is "the burden of sin" (Harold B. Lee, "Stand Ye in Holy Places," *Ensign*, July 1973, p. 122).

You can avoid that burden and all of the attending heartaches if you will but heed the standards laid down for you through the teachings of the Lord and the Lord's servants. One of the standards on which your happiness is based, now and in your future, is moral purity.

The world would tell you that this standard is old-fashioned and out-of-date. The world would have you accept a so-called new morality, which is nothing more than immorality. President Spencer W. Kimball reaffirmed that the eternal standard of chastity has not changed. Here are his words:

"The world may have its norm; the Church has a different one. . . . The world may countenance premarital sex experiences, but the Lord and his church condemn in no uncertain terms any and every sex relationship outside of marriage, and even indecent and uncontrolled ones within marriage. And so, though many self-styled authorities justify these practices as a normal release, the Church condemns them. . . . Such unholy practices were condemned by ancient prophets and are today condemned by the Church" (Spencer W. Kimball, *Faith Precedes the Miracle*, Salt Lake City: Deseret Book Co., 1972, p. 175).

This standard means keeping yourselves clean in body and mind. The Church has no double standard of morality. The moral code of heaven for both men and women is complete chastity before marriage and full fidelity after marriage.

For those not yet married, this uniform standard has been clearly defined by President Kimball.

"Among the most common sexual sins our young people commit are necking and petting. Not only do these improper relations often lead to fornication, pregnancy, and abortions—all ugly sins—but in and of themselves they are pernicious evils, and it is often difficult for youth to distinguish where one ends and another begins. They awaken lust and stir evil thoughts and sex desires. They are but parts of the whole family of related sins and indiscretions (Spencer W. Kimball, *The Miracle of Forgiveness*, Salt Lake City: Bookcraft, 1969, p. 65).

In the Church and kingdom of God, chastity will never be out-of-date, regardless of what the world may do or say. So we say to you young men and women—maintain your self-respect. Do not engage in intimacies that bring heartache and sorrow. You cannot build happy lives on immorality. "The first condition of happiness," said President David 0. McKay, "is a clear conscience" (Instructor, Nov. 1965, p. 422).

Second, I counsel you to stay close to your parents. There are some things which come only with mature adulthood, and one of these is wisdom. Young people, you need the wisdom of age, just as some of us older ones need your enthusiasm for life.

A young man, a few months out of college, got a job with an insurance company. He was full of enthusiasm and vigor—determined to sell insurance to all he met, including the farmers. He walked into a farmyard one lovely autumn morning and noticed an old farmer across the yard, somewhat stooped and bent, looking out over his field of grain. The salesman briskly walked over to the farmer and said, "Look up, my good man, there's much to live for."

The elderly farmer straightened up the best he could and replied: "Young man, you see that beautiful field of wheat?" The salesman acknowledged that indeed it was beautiful. "Do you notice that some of the heads are bent?"

"Yes," said the youth, "that's right; they are."

The old farmer said, "Those are the ones with the grain in them."

Your parents may become somewhat stooped and bent caring for you and your brothers and sisters. But just remember, those are the ones with the grain in them. Yes, young people, your parents, with their maturity of years and the experience you have not had, can provide wisdom, knowledge, and blessings to help you over life's pitfalls. You may find, as one young man did, that life's sweetest experiences come when you go to Mom and Dad for help.

Some time ago, a young man came to my office. He was about eighteen years of age and had some problems. There were no serious moral problems, but he was mixed up in his thinking and worried. He requested a blessing.

I said to him, "Have you ever asked your father to give you a blessing? Your father is a member of the Church, I assume?"

He said, "Yes, he is an elder, a rather inactive elder."

When I asked, "Do you love your father?" he replied, "Yes, President Benson, he is a good man. I love him. He doesn't attend to his priesthood duties as he should. He doesn't go to church regularly. I don't know that he is a tithe payer, but he is a good man, a good provider, a kind man."

I said, "How would you like to talk to him at an opportune time and ask him if he would give you a father's blessing?"

"Oh," he said, "I think that would frighten him."

I then said, "Are you willing to try it? I will be praying for you." He said, "All right, on that basis, I will."

A few days later he came back. He said, "Brother Benson, that's the sweetest thing that has happened in our family." He could hardly control his feelings as he told me what had happened. He said, "When the opportunity was right, I mentioned it to Father, and he replied, 'Son, do you really want me to give you a blessing?' I told him, 'Yes, Dad, I would like you to.' "

Then this young man said, "Brother Benson, he gave me one of the most beautiful blessings you could ever ask for. Mother sat there crying all during the blessing. When he got through there was a bond of appreciation and gratitude and love between us that we have never had in our home."

Draw close to Dad and Mom. When family prayer and home evening are suggested, don't pull away. Join in and make it real. Do your part to develop real family unity and family solidarity. In such homes there is no generation gap. This is another tool of the adversary—to drive children and parents apart. Yes, keep close to Dad and Mom.

Third, I counsel you, in the words of Jesus Christ, to "watch and pray always lest ye enter into temptation; for Satan desireth to have you, that he may sift you as wheat" (3 Ne. 18:18).

If you will earnestly seek guidance from your Heavenly Father, morning and evening, you will be given the strength to shun any temptation. President Heber J. Grant gave this timeless promise to the youth of the Church:

"I have little or no fear for the boy or the girl, the young man or the young woman, *who honestly and conscientiously supplicate God twice a day for the guidance of His Spirit.* I am sure that when temptation comes they will have the strength to overcome it by the inspiration that shall be given to them. Supplicating the Lord for the guidance of His Spirit places around us a safeguard, and if we earnestly and honestly seek the guidance of the Spirit of the Lord, I can assure you that we will receive it" (*Gospel Standards*, Salt Lake City: The Improvement Era, 1941, p. 26; italics added).

When you pray—when you talk to your Heavenly Father—do you really talk out your problems with Him? Do you let Him know your feelings, your doubts, your insecurities, your joys, your deepest desires—or is prayer merely an habitual expression with the same words and phrases. Do you ponder what you really mean to say? Do you take time to listen to the promptings of the Spirit? Answers to prayer come most often by a still voice and are discerned by our deepest, innermost feelings. I tell you that you can know the will of God concerning yourselves if you will take the time to pray and to listen.

Yes, beloved youth, you will have your trials and temptations through which you must pass, but there are great moments of eternity which lie ahead. You have our love and our confidence. We pray that you will be prepared for the reins of leadership. We say to you, "Arise and shine forth" (D&C 115:5) and be a light unto the world, a standard to others. You can live in the world and not partake of the sins of the world. You can live joyously, beautifully, unmarred by the ugliness of sin. This is our confidence in you.

Be glad, O Youth, your day is at the dawning,
For you the hours stretch long before the night;
What matter clouds be dark on the horizon?
Beyond them glow the rays of endless light.

Today the shadows may obscure your pathway,
Strange roads may beckon you on every side;
The bitterness of storm may bring a struggle,
To make you brave whatever may betide.

If deep within your heart you keep the vision—
The dream that nothing can erase or mar,
The promise of a fairer day tomorrow,
Will be for you a compass and a star.

Look to this day, arise in all your splendor,
And bear the standards of a world-to-be,
When hate and war, distress and desolation,
Give place to justice, love and liberty.

(Maude Osmond Cook, "Young Men Shall See Visions," *You Left Us with a Smile*, Salt Lake City: Melvin A. Cook Foundation, 1972, p. 59.)

I pray that you—the young and rising generation—will keep your bodies and minds clean, free from the contaminations of the world, that you will be fit and pure vessels to bear triumphantly the responsibilities of the kingdom of God in preparation for the second coming of our Savior.

From the June 1986 New Era.

THE ARMY OF THE LORD

President Thomas S. Monson

Some twenty-four years ago I was seated in the choir seats of the Assembly Hall situated on the southwest corner of Temple Square. The setting was stake conference. Elder Joseph Fielding Smith and Elder Alma Sonne had been assigned to reorganize our stake presidency. The Aaronic Priesthood, including members of bishoprics, were providing the music for the conference. Those of us who served as bishops were singing along with our young men. As we concluded singing our first selection, Elder Smith stepped to the pulpit and announced the names of the new stake presidency. I am confident the other members of the presidency had been made aware of their callings, but I had not. After reading my name, Elder Smith announced, "If Brother Monson is willing to respond to this call we shall be pleased to hear from him now." As I stood at the pulpit and gazed out on that sea of faces, I remembered the song we had just sung. Its title was "Have Courage, My Boy, to Say No." I selected as my acceptance theme "Have Courage, My Boy, to Say Yes."

The words of a better-known hymn describe you:

Behold! a royal army,
With banner, sword and shield,
Is marching forth to conquer,
On life's great battlefield;

Its ranks are filled with soldiers,
United, bold and strong,
Who follow their Commander,
And sing their joyful song:
Victory, victory,
Through him that redeemed us!
Victory, victory,
Through Jesus Christ our Lord!
(Hymns, 1985, no. 251.)

The priesthood represents a mighty army of righteousness—even a royal army. We are led by a prophet of God. In supreme command is our Lord and Savior, Jesus Christ. Our marching orders are clear. They are concise. Matthew describes our challenge in these words from the Master: "Go ye therefore, and teach all nations, baptizing them in the name of the Father, and of the Son, and of the Holy Ghost:

"Teaching them to observe all things whatsoever I have commanded you: and lo, I am with you alway, even unto the end of the world" (Matt. 28:19–20). Did those early disciples listen to this divine command? Mark records, "And they went forth, and preached every where, the Lord working with them" (Mark 16:20).

The command to go has not been rescinded. Rather, it has been reemphasized. Today thousands of missionaries are serving in response to the call. Additional thousands will soon respond. New missions are being created. What a thrilling and challenging time in which to live!

You who hold the Aaronic Priesthood and honor it have been reserved for this special period in history. The harvest truly is great. Let there be no mistake about it; the opportunity of a lifetime is yours. The blessings of eternity await you. How might you best respond? May I suggest you cultivate three virtues, namely—

1. A desire to serve.
2. The patience to prepare.
3. A willingness to labor.

By so doing, you will ever be found part of that royal army of the Lord. Let us consider, individually, each of these three virtues.

First, a desire to serve. Remember the qualifying statement of the Master, "Behold, the Lord requireth the heart and a willing mind" (D&C 64:34). A latter-day minister advised: "Until willingness overflows obligation, men fight as conscripts rather than following the flag as patriots. Duty is never worthily performed until it is performed by one who would gladly do more if only he could."

Isn't it appropriate that you do not call yourselves to the missionary work? Isn't it wise that your parents do not call you? Rather, you are called of God by prophecy and by revelation. Your call bears the signature of the President of the Church.

It was my privilege to serve for many years with President Spencer W. Kimball when he was chairman of the Missionary Executive Committee of the Church. Those never-to-be-forgotten missionary assignment meetings were filled with inspiration and occasionally interspersed with humor. Well do I remember the recommendation form for one prospective missionary on which the bishop had written: "This young man is very close to his mother. She wonders if he might be assigned to a mission close to home in California so that she can visit him on occasion and telephone him weekly." As I read aloud this comment, I awaited from President Kimball the pronouncement of a designated assignment. I noticed a twinkle in his eye and a sweet smile cross his lips as he said, without additional comment, "Assign him to the Johannesburg South Africa Mission."

Too numerous to mention are the many instances where a particular call proved providential. This I know—divine inspiration attends such sacred assignments. We, with you, acknowledge the truth stated so simply in the Doctrine and Covenants: "If ye have desires to serve God ye are called to the work" (D&C 4:3).

Second, the patience to prepare. Preparation for a mission is not a spur-of-the-moment matter. It began before you can remember. Every class in Primary, Sunday School, seminary—each priesthood assignment—had a larger application. Silently, almost imperceptibly, a life was molded, a career commenced, a man made. Said the poet:

Who touches a boy by the Master's plan
Is shaping the course of a future man.

What a challenge is the calling to be an adviser to a quorum of boys. Advisers, do you really think about your opportunity? Do you pray? Do you prepare? Do you prepare your boys?

As a boy of fifteen I was called to preside over a quorum of teachers. Our adviser was interested in us, and we knew it. One day he said to me, "Tom, you enjoy raising pigeons, don't you?"

I responded with a warm "Yes."

Then he proffered, "How would you like me to give you a pair of purebred Birmingham Roller pigeons?"

This time I answered, "Yes, sir!" You see, the pigeons I had were just the common variety trapped on the roof of the Grant Elementary School.

He invited me to come to his home the next evening. The next day was one of the longest in my young life. I was awaiting my adviser's return from work an hour before he arrived. He took me to his loft, which was in a small barn at the rear of his yard. As I looked at the most beautiful pigeons I had yet seen, he said, "Select any male, and I will give you a female which is different from any other pigeon in the world." I made my selection. He then placed in my hand a tiny hen. I asked what made her so different. He responded, "Look carefully, and you'll notice that she has but one eye." Sure enough, one eye was missing, a cat having done the damage. "Take them home to your loft," he counseled. "Keep them in for about ten days and then turn them out to see if they will remain at your place."

I followed his instructions. Upon releasing them, the male pigeon strutted about the roof of the loft, then returned inside to eat. But the one-eyed female was gone in an instant. I called Harold, my adviser, and asked: "Did that one-eyed pigeon return to your loft?"

"Come on over," said he, "and we'll have a look."

As we walked from his kitchen door to the loft, my adviser commented, "Tom, you are the president of the teachers quorum." This I already knew. Then he added, "What are you going to do to activate Bob?"

I answered, "I'll have him at quorum meeting this week."

Then he reached up to a special nest and handed to me the one-eyed pigeon. "Keep her in a few days and try again." This I did, and once more she disappeared. Again the experience, "Come on over and we'll see if she returned here." Came the comment as we walked to the loft, "Congratulations on getting Bob to priesthood meeting. Now what are you and Bob going to do to activate Bill?"

"We'll have him there this week," I volunteered.

This experience was repeated over and over again. I was a grown man before I fully realized that, indeed, Harold, my adviser, had given me a special pigeon: the only bird in his loft he knew would return every time she was released. It was his inspired way of having an ideal personal priesthood interview with the teachers quorum president every two weeks. I owe a lot to that one-eyed pigeon. I owe more to that quorum adviser. He had the patience to help me prepare for opportunities which lay ahead.

Third, a willingness to labor. Missionary work is difficult. It will tax your energies. It will strain your capacity. It will demand your best effort—frequently, a second effort. Remember, the race goeth "not to the swift, nor the battle to the strong" (Eccl. 9:11)—but to him who endures to the end. Determine to—

Stick to your task till it sticks to you.
Beginners are many, but enders are few.
Honor, power, place and praise
Will always come to the one who stays.
Stick to your task till it sticks to you;
Bend at it, sweat at it, smile at it, too—
For out of the bend and the sweat and the smile
Will come life's victories after awhile.

During the final phases of World War II, I turned eighteen and was ordained an elder—one week before I departed for active duty with the Navy. A member of my ward bishopric was at the train station to bid me farewell. Just before train time, he placed in my hand a book. Its title, the Missionary Handbook. I laughed and commented, "I'm not going on a mission." He answered, "Take it anyway. It may come in handy."

It did. During basic training our company commander instructed us concerning how we might best pack our clothing in a large sea bag. He advised, "If you have a hard, rectangular object you can place in the bottom of the bag, your clothes will stay more firm." I suddenly remembered just the right rectangular object—the Missionary Handbook. Thus it served for twelve weeks.

The night preceding our Christmas leave our thoughts were, as always, on home. The barracks were quiet. Suddenly I became aware that my buddy in the adjoining bunk—a Mormon boy, Leland Merrill—was moaning with pain. I asked, "What's the matter, Merrill?"

He replied, "I'm sick. I'm really sick."

I advised him to go to the base dispensary, but he answered

knowingly that such a course would prevent him from being home for Christmas.

The hours lengthened; his groans grew louder. Then, in desperation, he whispered, "Monson, Monson, aren't you an elder?" I acknowledged this to be so; whereupon he asked, "Give me a blessing."

I became very much aware that I had never given a blessing. I had never received such a blessing; I had never witnessed a blessing being given. My prayer to God was a plea for help. The answer came: "Look in the bottom of the sea bag." Thus, at 2:00 A.M. I emptied on the deck the contents of the bag. I then took to the night-light that hard, rectangular object, the *Missionary Handbook*, and read how one blesses the sick. With about sixty curious sailors looking on, I proceeded with the blessing. Before I could stow my gear, Leland Merrill was sleeping like a child.

The next morning Merrill smilingly turned to me and said, "Monson, I'm glad you hold the priesthood." His gladness was only surpassed by my gratitude.

Future missionaries, may our Heavenly Father bless you with a desire to serve, the patience to prepare, and a willingness to labor, that you and all who comprise this royal army of the Lord may merit his promise: "I will go before your face. I will be on your right hand and on your left, and my Spirit shall be in your hearts, and mine angels round about you, to bear you up" (D&C 84:88).

A conference address from the May 1979 Ensign.

A PRIESTHOOD OF PREPARATION

Elder Boyd K. Packer

I have seven sons, and I have learned a great deal from them and have had to depend a great deal upon them. Sometimes we have had another holder of the Melchizedek Priesthood at home; often we have not. Our elders have been on missions, or they are married; so the priesthood in our home has been Aaronic Priesthood. I am away a great deal and am very grateful for our young sons who hold the priesthood.

I want to talk to you young men about this priesthood and tell you a story or two from our family experience. Several years ago our sons would spend their time during the summer on their grandfather's ranch. One of our sons had a horse. It had been given to him when it was born. It had been running with a wild herd of horses on the ranch. It was now two years old, time that it could be broken to ride. Early one summer we went to the ranch. It took all day to get the horses into the corral. Finally we had my son's horse in a chute and put a heavy halter on it. We put a big rope on it and tied it to a big post. "Now the horse must stay there for two or three days," I told him, "until it quits fighting the rope, until it settles down." We worked with it during the morning, and then we went in to eat. He hurried with his meal and then went out to his horse. He was fourteen. He loved that horse.

Just as we finished the meal, I heard a noise, and I heard him shout. I knew what had happened. He had untied the horse. I had told him not to, but he was going to work with it. In order to hold the horse, he had wrapped the rope around his wrist. As I came out the door, I saw that horse run by. My son was running after it with great big steps, pulled by the horse; and then he fell. If the horse had turned right, it would have gone out the gate into the mountains. It turned left and was cornered by two fences. While it was trying to find its way out, I got the rope off my boy's wrist and the end of the rope around the post. He was bruised but not badly hurt.

In a little while we had the horse tied up again, and we sat down for a father and son lesson. I said to him this: "My boy, if you are ever going to control that horse, you will have to use something besides your muscles. The horse is bigger than you are. Someday you can ride that horse, but it will have to be trained. You cannot train it with your muscles. It is bigger than you are; it is stronger than you are; and it is wild."

Two years later we went to the ranch in the spring. This horse had been running all winter with the herd. We went to find it. We found the herd of horses down by the river. I knew if we went too close, they would run. So this boy and his sister took a bucket with some oats and walked quietly to the edge of the meadow. The horses began to move away slowly. Then he whistled, and his horse came out of the herd and trotted up to my boy. We had learned a great lesson. Much had happened in those two years. He had used more than his muscles.

After that near accident had happened, he was frightened. He had disobeyed. And he said, "Dad, what should we do?" And I said, "This is the way we will do it. And one day that horse will run up to you." He had been prepared and had learned a great lesson.

The Aaronic Priesthood is the preparatory priesthood. It is the lesser priesthood. Preparatory for what? It is to prepare young men to hold the Melchizedek Priesthood. It is to prepare young men for life. It is to train them to be leaders. It is to train them in obedience. It is to train them to get control of things that are bigger than they are. It is to show them how to use more than their muscles.

Now, when you are ordained a deacon at age twelve, you join a quorum. Oh, what a marvelous blessing it is to belong to a quorum! All of your life you will belong to a quorum: the deacons quorum with twelve members, the teachers with twenty-four members, the priests quorum with forty-eight members. Then if you are faithful and worthy, you will be ordained to the Melchizedek Priesthood or the higher priesthood. But we are talking to the boys of the Aaronic Priesthood. The Aaronic Priesthood is to prepare us for the Melchizedek Priesthood. We are to learn how to do things in the same way we will do them when we hold the Melchizedek Priesthood.

Let me tell you about this boy again. Now he is married. He has graduated with a degree in engineering, and he has left to go away to a big city. He and his wife were nervous—a new job, a new home, away from the family.

He told me these two experiences. He worked in a large room with a lot of engineers. After he had been there for two months, he was getting things ready so that he could leave his work on time. We had taught him to arrive at work a little early and to stay a little after time, to do a little extra. But this day he wanted to get away right on time. One of the other engineers asked him where he was going.

"What are you in such a hurry for?"

"Well, we are going to a dinner tonight."

"What kind of a dinner?"

"It's a quorum dinner. We are taking our wives to a special dinner and a social."

The other engineer shook his head. "I don't understand you. I've been here two years; I don't know anybody yet. My wife and I are still just by ourselves. You've been here for two months. Already you've been invited to dinner."

The next experience. One day one of the engineers asked if my son would help him move. "We found a better apartment. Saturday we are going to move. I need some help. Will you help me?" Our son said, "Why, of course." And then his wife made some bread for them and prepared a meal. He helped them move. Then he said this: "Dad, I've been thinking about that. He hardly knows me. I hardly knew who he was." And he said, "If I'm the one who was the closest to him, the one he would dare to ask help him move, he doesn't have anybody." And he said, "Look what I have."

When he and his wife arrived in the new city, they went to church. He went to *his* quorum; he belonged the day he walked in. A quorum—to sustain one another, to help one another. A quorum of the priesthood. You boys of the Aaronic Priesthood can begin to prepare now. You're trained to help others—to gather the fast offerings; to take care of other assignments, the sacrament, home teaching; to get you trained to help others. Why? You belong to a quorum. A quorum. The word *quorum* is a marvelous word. In the Church, quorums have never yet fully come into their own.

It is a tremendous honor to belong to a quorum. To be called to preside over a quorum is a signal responsibility. To be called as the secretary of a quorum, or to teach a quorum, is a tremendous responsibility. Do you know where the word *quorum* comes from? It isn't in the Old Testament or the New Testament. It comes from ancient Rome. When they would form a commission of great importance to perform a great work, they would appoint the members of this commission. And they would send them their certificate. And on that certificate the word *quorum* would appear. It would tell what the commission was going to do, how important it was, that great men were being chosen, and then it would contain these words: *Quorum vos unum*, meaning, "You are to be one."

My young brethren, you belong to quorums. What a tremendous opportunity! You can learn to control life. You can learn to be in charge, to take care of your life and to assist others. I am grateful to have held the Aaronic Priesthood, and to still hold it. I am more grateful that my sons have held it and grateful that you can hold it. God bless you, my boys. May the Spirit of the Lord rest upon you. The gospel is true. The priesthood is a great opportunity.

From the May 1979 New Era.

THE OATH AND COVENANT OF THE PRIESTHOOD

Elder Carlos E. Asay

Of all the holy agreements pertaining to the gospel of Jesus Christ, few, if any, would transcend in importance the oath and covenant of the priesthood. It is certainly one of the most sacred agreements, for it involves the sharing of heavenly powers and man's upward reaching toward eternal goals. None of us can afford to be ignorant of the terms of this contract. To do so might cause us to miss the mark in our performance of duty and result in the forfeiture of promised blessings.

A gospel covenant is a holy contract. "God in his good pleasure fixes the terms, which man accepts" (Bible Dictionary, LDS ed., s.v. "covenant").

The two parties to the priesthood covenant are man and God. Man covenants to do certain things or meet certain conditions; God cites promises that he will give in return.

Man's Covenant

1. Receive the Melchizedek Priesthood in good faith. When a man has the Melchizedek Priesthood conferred upon him, he is expected to *receive* it in good faith. The word *receive* is used generously in the Doctrine and Covenants verses that describe the oath and covenant of the priesthood:

"All they who receive this priesthood receive me, saith the Lord; . . .

"And he that receiveth me receiveth my Father;

"And he that receiveth my Father receiveth my Father's kingdom" (D&C 84:35, 37–38).

As people are confirmed members of the Church, those in authority lay hands upon their heads and command, "Receive the Holy Ghost." Does not the same apply to the conferral of priesthood power? Several years ago, my father laid his hands upon my head to confer upon me the Melchizedek Priesthood and, as described in the Old Testament, to "put some of [his] honour upon [me] . . . and gave [me] a charge" (see Num. 27:18–23). I knew that he had power to bestow, I knew that that power was real, and I knew the ultimate source of that power. So I received the holy priesthood in good faith.

2. Magnify callings. President Kimball defines *priesthood*, in part, as "the means whereby the Lord acts through men to save souls" (*Ensign*, June 1975, p. 3). This definition suggests action, not inaction. It implies that priesthood power is to be exercised in behalf of other people; it is not something to sit upon or to simply glory in. It suggests that priesthood callings are to be *magnified*.

The transcendent blessings of the priesthood do not come by ordination alone. We are instructed:

"Ordination to the priesthood is a prerequisite to receiving [blessings], but it does not guarantee them. For a man actually to obtain them, he must faithfully discharge the obligation which is placed upon him when he receives the priesthood" (Marion G. Romney, in Conference Report, Apr. 1962, p. 17).

What does it mean to magnify one's calling? According to *Webster's Third New International Dictionary*, "to magnify" is "to increase the importance of: cause to be held in greater esteem or respect . . . to make greater." One magnifies a calling —

• By learning one's duty and executing it fully (see D&C 107:99–100).

• By giving one's best effort in assigned fields of labor.

• By consecrating one's time, talents, and means to the Lord's work as called upon by our leaders and the whisperings of the Spirit (see Spencer W. Kimball, *Ensign*, Mar. 1985, p. 5).

• By teaching and exemplifying truth.

Jacob, the Book of Mormon prophet, testified, "We did magnify our office unto the Lord, taking upon us the responsibility, . . . [teaching] them the word of God with all diligence; . . . [and] laboring with our might" (Jacob 1:19).

I underscore the words *taking responsibility, teaching the word of God,* and *laboring with might* in this inspired quotation. These are critical actions related to the exercise of priesthood power.

3. Obey the commandments. In the revelation on priesthood, we read, "And I now give unto you a commandment . . . to give diligent heed to the words of eternal life" (D&C 84:43). "To give diligent heed," I believe, includes to *obey* the commandments.

No commandment or requirement of the gospel is non-essential. Each has its place, and all are to be respected. Not one is to be trifled with or placed aside as inconvenient.

A person who chooses to obey one commandment and ignore others is as foolish as the driver who adheres strictly to the posted speed limit but runs every stop sign and flaunts other rules of the road.

Let us remember that with every commandment, God has promised a blessing. If we expect to claim the blessing, we must keep the commandment. Otherwise, if we ignore or break the commandment, we are cursed by losing the blessing (see Deut. 11:26–28). It is a very simple but serious arrangement.

4. Live by every word of God. Addressing priesthood bearers, the Lord says, "For you shall *live* by every word that proceedeth forth from the mouth of God" (D&C 84:44; italics added). This statement reinforces the need for obedience. It also suggests the need to know the word of the Lord.

Words of eternal life come from one source: God. They are made available to us through the fountain of the holy scriptures and the fountain of living prophets and reconfirmed by personal revelation through the power of the Holy Ghost.

When we search the scriptures, we sit at the feet of prophets like Abraham, Isaiah, Peter, Paul, Nephi, Moroni, and Joseph Smith. These men received revelations in a former day and have much wisdom to share with us. Their counsel may be likened to a light positioned behind us. That light helps us understand things of the past and gives us partial vision for the future.

To receive added light, light positioned over and ahead of us, we must sit at the feet of living prophets. None of us need stumble along the way or depart from the path in the presence of such light. All we need to do is keep our eyes upon the prophets, heed their warnings, and live by their inspired words.

Men of the priesthood should burn these words in their minds: "What I the Lord have spoken, I have spoken, and I excuse not myself; . . . my word . . . shall all be fulfilled, whether by mine own voice or by the voice of my servants, it is the same" (D&C 1:38; see also vs. 11–14).

I have indicated that a man who receives the Melchizedek Priesthood agrees (1) to receive it in good faith, (2) to magnify callings given, (3) to obey all the commandments, and (4) to live by every word of God. These four expectations compose man's covenant as applied to the oath and covenant of the priesthood.

Next, let's consider God's promises and oath. You might ask, "If I fulfill my terms of the agreement, what has God promised in return?" Let us consider three promises:

God's Promises and Oath

Promise 1. We will be sanctified by the Spirit. Note these words:

"For whoso is faithful unto the obtaining these two priesthoods of which I have spoken [Aaronic and Melchizedek Priesthood], and the magnifying their calling, are sanctified by the Spirit unto the renewing of their bodies" (D&C 84:33).

On one occasion, President Hugh B. Brown testified that President David O. McKay had been sanctified by the Spirit unto the renewing of his body. And, he added, "Some of the rest of us are better off today than we were many years ago so far as physical health is concerned — and we attribute that fact to [the Lord's] blessing" (in Conference Report, Apr. 1963, p. 90).

Many of us have felt the influence of this "renewal promise." Without it, scores of our assignments might have gone unfinished.

Promise 2: We will be numbered with the elect of God. It is said of those who receive the holy priesthood and remain true to their covenants, "They become the sons of Moses and of Aaron and the seed of Abraham, and the church and kingdom, and the elect of God" (D&C 84:34).

Elder Bruce R. McConkie explains:

"These are the portion of church members who are striving with all their hearts to keep the fulness of the gospel law in this life so that they can become inheritors of the fulness of gospel rewards in the life to come" (*Mormon Doctrine*, 2d ed., Salt Lake City: Bookcraft, 1966, p. 217).

We do not become saints automatically by entering the waters of baptism. We become saints, in the true sense of the word, as we live saintly lives and cultivate Christlike attributes. Similarly, we do not become the elect of God instantaneously by receiving the priesthood. Such honor will come only so fast as we remember and perform according to the priesthood covenant.

Promise 3: We will be given all that God has. This all-encompassing promise is stated by Christ in these words: "All that my Father hath shall be given unto him" (D&C 84:38).

Few of us, I suppose, can comprehend all that this promise means. Even though we know that it includes eternal life, or the inheritance of exaltation, still it is so great and so wonderful that it defies proper explanation. It is sufficient for me to know that God in heaven is my Father and that he will bless me with all he has to offer, if I prove myself to be a faithful son.

I stand in humble adoration of my Maker when I realize that he has sworn and confirmed his part of the agreement with an oath (see Heb. 6:13–17). He will never fall short of his promise, nor will he void it or compromise it in the slightest degree.

Perhaps I can place in clearer perspective all that I have said about the oath and covenant of the priesthood by relating a story based on a true experience.

The son of a very wealthy man was called to serve a full-time mission. He entered the mission field and began his work. At first things went well; however, as he met rejections and as other challenges of finding and teaching surfaced, the young man's faith wavered.

Mission associates gave encouragement, but it did not seem to help. One day the young man announced to the mission president that he was abandoning his call; he was returning home. The mission president did all within his power to dissuade the missionary. It was to no avail.

When word of the missionary's decision reached the father, he obtained permission to visit his son in the mission field. In one of many tense conversations, the father said, "My son, I have lived for the day when you would serve a full-time mission. I did so because I love you and I love God. And I know that there is no work more essential than that of teaching truth to the peoples of the world."

Somewhat sobered by his father's words, the son replied, "Dad, I didn't realize that a mission meant so much to you."

"It means everything to me," the father declared. Then he added with some emotion, "All my life I have worked and saved with one person in mind: you. And my one goal has been to provide you a decent inheritance."

"But Dad," the son interjected, "the work is difficult and I don't enjoy . . . "

The father didn't allow him to finish his sentence. Instead he asked, "How can I trust my businesses to your care if you cannot prove yourself by serving the Lord for two short years?"

There was an awkward pause as the son pondered the father's question and studied his anxious countenance.

Then with measured words, the father promised, "My son, my only heir, if you will be faithful in this calling and prove yourself worthy in every respect, all that I possess will be yours."

Noticeably touched by these earnest pleadings, the son rose to his feet, embraced his father, and sobbed, "I will stay."

The son did stay in the mission field; he did serve faithfully from that day forward. And yes, in due time, he received from his father the promised inheritance, even all that his father had to share.

My brethren, we are the sons of God. He has endowed us with his power, and he has called each of us to serve missions in a place called mortality. Our missions mean very much to him, and they should mean everything to us. In this mortal life, we are to prove ourselves worthy of his love and worthy of the inheritance he has offered.

What is that inheritance? It is all that he has, even eternal life. This blessed and promised gift will be ours only if we keep the covenants, particularly the covenant of the priesthood, and remain faithful to the end.

A conference address from the November 1985 Ensign.

BEAR TRACKS

Elder Dean L. Larsen

I grew up in a small community in northern Utah, Hyrum, which was named after Hyrum Smith, brother of the Prophet Joseph Smith. During my growing-up years, Hyrum had a population of about 1,500 people. The rural setting permitted us to have a barn with horses and cows, a pasture for the animals, a large garden, and some of the other necessities that went along with country living. We were almost self-sufficient when it came to producing food for the family, and that was a great asset for a family of nine that was trying to survive on the small salary my father received as a school teacher. By being resourceful, we were somehow able to make ends meet.

Our food supply usually contained venison that my father and older brothers provided for us during the big game season in the late fall—usually during October. The deer hunt was an important event for the family, not only because of the meat that would go into our cold-storage locker, but also because it was an exciting adventure. The boys and men in the family, and sometimes the girls as well, would go into the mountains and make camp for several days. The outing, as much as the hunting, made this an enjoyable event each year. Even now, as my enthusiasm for hunting has faded, I recall with the fondest of memories those eventful days in the mountains with family and loved ones, when the air was crisp and full of the scent of newly fallen leaves. It was part of the fiber of our lives.

After I had married and had started a teaching career of my own in the Big Horn Basin of Wyoming, the pattern of going into the mountains each fall during the big game season continued. With a growing family to care for, I found that the addition of a deer and an elk to our winter's food supply was a big help. The Wyoming mountain country was even more primitive and vast than the Utah mountains where I had spent so much time as a young man. It was a marvelous place to live for someone who loved the outdoors as much as I did.

During one of those hunting seasons in Wyoming, I had an experience that taught me an important lesson—one that I have always remembered. It occurred in a year when the weather had been rather unusual. The early snows that generally fall in the high country by late September had not come. The days remained warm and sunny even into mid-October when the big game season opened. The deer and elk stayed in the more remote high country, making it very difficult for the hunters to get to them.

Finally, late in the season, the snows came, and I made plans with a friend to go into the Big Horn Mountains close to the border between Montana and Wyoming for a last try at finding an elk. We traveled in his four-wheel drive vehicle to a spot at an elevation of about 9,000 feet where the Little Big Horn River has its beginning. A new blanket of snow almost one foot in depth covered the ground. We began our hunt just as the first daylight showed over the eastern ridges. We decided to separate from one another, designating a point of the mountain at some distance where we would meet later in the day.

As I crossed over the small stream near which we had left our vehicle and started into the timber on the opposite slope I came to some fresh tracks in the new snow. They were bear tracks— big ones! The tracks came as something of a surprise to me. Bear are not uncommon in much of the mountain country of Wyoming and they are numerous enough that they are considered legal game. However, bear were not common in the Big Horn Mountains, and this sudden encounter with the fresh tracks filled my mind with some interesting possibilities. I had never hunted for a bear; in fact, I had never had the inclination to do so. The meat would have been of no use to me.

This bear was no immediate threat to my companion or to me. If he were still in the area and aware of our presence, he was likely trying to remove himself from any confrontation with us. Still, as I studied the tracks and discovered how fresh they were, my thoughts continued to stir me. I confess that I began to have visions of a bearskin rug for our home. Since the tracks were going in about the same direction I had intended to go, I decided to follow them.

Within a hundred yards or so I came to a place where the snow was scattered about among traces of blood and deer hair. I could tell that one way or another, the bear had taken a deer in that place that morning. The trail that was left was easy to follow as the bear had partly carried and partly dragged the deer through the brush and into a thicket of pines and spruce. There I found the deer. Its head and horns had caught in the juncture of some limbs of a fallen tree, and the bear had not stayed to dislodge it. Perhaps my coming on the scene had affected that decision.

As I continued to follow the trail of the bear, I climbed up a steep slope where the going was made more difficult by the dense underbrush. I put my rifle with its leather sling over my shoulder and used my hands as well as my feet to force my way up the incline. Every few yards I stopped to catch my breath and rest a moment.

During one of these pauses I looked about me and assessed my situation. Because of the density of the undergrowth, I was aware that it would be impossible for me to get a clear shot at anything more than eight or ten yards away. I began to wonder who would have the greater advantage if I were to come upon the bear.

As these thoughts went through my mind, I felt a most interesting sensation come over me. I experienced a tingling in my skin, and I could feel the hair rise on the back of my neck. I had the strong impression that I was in grave danger and that I should leave the area immediately. The impression was so powerful that I got to my feet, went back down the slope to where the country was more open, and there felt that I was in better control of things. Any further desire to pursue the bear evaporated, and I went about the business for which my friend and I had gone into the mountains that day.

I have reflected on that experience from time to time through the intervening years. Occasionally I have been confronted with opportunities to pursue some venture or activity that seemed to offer the possibility of excitement or adventure. Always when danger or a threat to my physical or spiritual well-being has accompanied these opportunities, I have felt some of the same impressions and warning signals that came to me that day in the mountains of Wyoming. They have not always been as powerful as they were there on the slopes of the Little Big Horn, but they are clear enough that they are not easy to ignore. I have learned that whenever I see "bear tracks," figuratively speaking, it is wise to check for the warning signals that penetrate one's conscience. These signals can save us from much heartache and difficulty.

Young people who face the prospect of growing up and making their way in today's world will likely encounter many "bear tracks" to entice them into the thickets of worldly excitement and pleasure. These enticements can assume many forms. Some of them can appear at first glance to be relatively harmless and innocent. They can be encountered in almost any setting—even in the sanctuary of our own homes. They can appear in the written word, in newspapers, magazines, and books. Some of them take a graphic form with illustrations or photographs. Some penetrate our thoughts and sensitivities through music, while others use all of the sophistication of modern electronic audio and visual technology, including television and the movies. Sometimes we follow "bear tracks" in the indiscretions we display in our relationships with each other that lead to immoral behavior. Many have followed "bear tracks" into the nightmarish world of drug abuse and addiction.

I remember reading several years ago of a man who had gone into the wilderness area of the state of Montana with a companion on a big game hunt. The hunters came upon a grizzly bear at rather close range, and one of the men fired at the bear and wounded it. In a rage the huge animal charged the hunters. One of them, in panic and in a desperate attempt to save himself, climbed into the lower branches of a small tree close by. The tree was not large enough to support the man's weight and hold him beyond the reach of the bear's powerful claws and jaws. Before his companion could destroy the bear, it had inflicted such serious injuries on the treed hunter that it was necessary to amputate both his legs in order to save his life.

Those who follow the figurative "bear tracks" to which I have alluded earlier must be aware that they inevitably lead to danger. Some of these dangers can be fatal to spirituality and faith; others can cause serious injury to true happiness and self-respect from which it is difficult to recover. Willfully following "bear tracks" can have tragic consequences.

My experience has taught me that the best way to avoid the dangers into which "bear tracks" can lead us is to avoid following them. Respond to the warning signals that come through the promptings of the Holy Spirit; escape to safe ground where we are in control of the situation and where we can merit the protecting and preserving powers that our Heavenly Father has promised to those who obey him.

As we do this, we will find a security and peace of mind that are more valuable than all of the thrill and excitement that pursuing "bear tracks" could ever bring. In addition, we will be able to continue along the pathway to eternal happiness with confidence that we are eligible for every good blessing that may be necessary to guard us and preserve us from the forces that seek to do us injury and hedge up the way.

From the January-February 1983 New Era.

DECIDE
TO DECIDE

Elder Rex D. Pinegar

I am grateful for my assignment with the young men of the Church. Those in the Aaronic Priesthood quorums of the Church are our future missionaries, Church leaders, and leaders in the world. With so great an opportunity, I desire today to speak to this vast army of youth about their power to be whatever they decide to be.

In the summer of 1980 I had the unforgettable experience of camping with twenty-six hundred wonderful Aaronic Priesthood Young Men and their leaders. Amid a colorful array of tents and Boy Scout uniforms, the encampment took the shape of a giant twelve-spoked wheel. Each spoke housed one of Israel's twelve "tribes." The six days of camping at the Florida Deseret Ranch provided camping skills, special demonstrations, tests of physical fitness, inspirational programs, and numerous other activities (not to mention consumption of fifty-eight hundred gallons of milk, sixty-three thousand pounds of ice, one thousand cases of soft drinks, and one and one-half tons of bread). The young men and their priesthood leaders participated together, focusing upon priesthood objectives.

On the first evening at dusk, with each "tribe" in place, all of "Israel" marched to an arena for the opening campfire. The golden rays of sunset formed a magnificent backdrop for the mile-long line of young men as they marched two abreast toward the arena. With colorful banners held aloft, the modern-day sons of Israel passed beneath an archway emblazoned with the Scout Promise: "On My Honor." Sentries stood holding torch-lighted signs inscribed with the Scout Oath and Law and Aaronic Priesthood objectives. As the priesthood leaders led their young men past these sentries, it was anticipated that each young man would make a personal commitment to strive daily toward eternal life, to be a worthy priesthood bearer, worthy to serve a mission; worthy to marry in the temple.

The decisions made that night were followed up during the next four days by special "mountaintop" experiences. The leaders of ancient Israel often went to a designated mountaintop to receive special instruction from the Lord. It was planned that these "Israelite" priesthood bearers would prepare themselves to come to especially designated locations at the encampment where they might receive spiritual guidance and counsel. Here they learned that, having committed themselves to live the basic principles of the gospel, they had also committed themselves to make other important decisions regarding such things as being morally clean, being honest in word and deed, keeping the Word of Wisdom, and so forth.

These are some of the "certain things" to which President Kimball referred in a conference address:

"We hope we can help our young men and young women to realize, even sooner than they do now, that they need to make *certain* decisions only *once*. . . . We can push some things away from us once and have done with them! We can make a single decision about certain things that we will incorporate in our lives and then make them ours—without having to brood and redecide a hundred times what it is we will do and what we will not do.

" . . . My young brothers, if you have not done so yet, decide to decide!" (*Ensign*, May 1976, p. 46; italics added).

You can do it, my young brethren. You can become the men of righteousness and stature that your dreams and ambitions hold up before you. To accomplish this objective, you need to make some important decisions now, early in your life. This *is* the time to decide to decide!

First, decide to set goals. In his same conference address, President Kimball said:

"It is most appropriate for Aaronic Priesthood youth, as well as Melchizedek Priesthood men [and I would add, the women of the Church], to quietly, and with determination, set some serious personal goals in which they will seek to improve by selecting certain things that they will accomplish within a specified period of time" (*Ensign*, May 1976, p. 46).

A friend of mine helped his son set goals in this manner. Don asked his son what he wanted to be, whom he would want to be like. His son named a member of the ward who lived nearby, a man he had admired for some time. Don drove his son to where the man lived.

As they sat in their automobile in front of his home, they observed the man's possessions and his way of life. They also discussed his kindness and generosity, his good name and integrity. They discussed the price their neighbor had paid to become what he was: the years of hard work, the schooling and training required, the sacrifices made, the challenges encountered. The affluence and seeming ease with which he now lived had come about as the result of diligent toil toward his righteous goals and the blessings of the Lord.

The son selected other men whom he deemed models of successful and righteous living and learned from a wise father the stories of their lives. Thereupon at an early age he set his own goal of what he wanted to become. And with his goal before him as a guide by which to make other decisions along the way, he was prepared to stay on his chosen course.

Next, decide to work. Work is necessary if you are to reach your goal. J. Paul Getty, considered to be at one time one of the world's wealthiest men, gave this formula for success: "Rise early, work late, and strike oil!" Mr. Getty has also made the thought-provoking comment that "it is possible for a man to get on a train that goes sixty miles per hour and say to himself, 'I am going sixty miles per hour.' But it is not true. Unless he is moving ahead on his own power, he is standing still" (J. Paul Getty, *Reader's Digest*, Sept. 1980, p. 94).

Isaac Stern, the world-famous musician-violinist, was asked by a television talk show host at what point in his life he determined to devote his energies toward a career as a concert violinist. Mr. Stern told of having given his first concert in San Francisco at a young age. Music critics were extremely impressed and predicted a fine future for the promising young talent. With this encouragement, Isaac Stern began preparations for another concert a year later in New York City. The critics were not so kind to him there. It would require a tremendous amount of work, they judged, if Isaac Stern were to achieve success as a soloist.

Dejected and discouraged, the young Mr. Stern boarded one

of New York City's double-decker buses and rode it up and down Manhattan a number of times. He was, in his words, "crying inside" as he tried to decide where he was going from there. Were his critics correct? Had he gone as far as he was capable of going? Should he now seek a profession as just another member of an orchestra?

After his fourth ride through the city, he returned to his apartment where his Mother was waiting. He had made his decision. "I am going to *work*, Mother—*work* at my music until it *works for me*." Today Isaac Stern is acclaimed as one of the finest violinists in the world. Work is a principle with a blessing. Work builds us physically and spiritually. It increases both our strength of body and our strength of character.

A basketball coach claimed, "If you find a man on top of a mountain, he didn't fall there." If you and I are to reach the summit of our divine potential, we must work each step of the way. The path may be rugged, difficult, unheralded; but it can be successfully climbed if we are willing to work with all our strength and commitment.

Next, decide to believe. Believe in God. Believe in yourself. Believe that God is very interested in you as an individual, that he is anxious for you to succeed. He has provided in the gospel of his Son Jesus Christ the sure pattern for ultimate success.

When our lives are consistent with his gospel, we receive confidence through his Spirit to meet the challenges of each day. We can say with Nephi: "The Lord is able to do all things according to his will, for the children of men, if it so be that they exercise faith in him. . . . Wherefore, let us be faithful to him" (1 Ne. 7:12).

The Prophet Joseph Smith's belief in God, his faith in God's interest in him, gave him the courage and optimism to say:

"Never get discouraged, whatever difficulties might surround [you]. If [you were] sunk in the lowest pit of Nova Scotia, and all the Rocky Mountains piled on top of [you], [you] ought not to be discouraged, but hang on, exercise faith and keep up good courage and [you] should come out on top of the heap" (George A. Smith's journal, quoted by Preston Nibley in *Church Section*, 12 Mar. 1950, p. 16).

You, our beloved young men and women, are in the most critical period of life. Youth is the time when habits are formed, when ideas are adopted. It is the time of decision. Decide today to heed these words of our prophet: "Decide to decide!"

Decide to make decisions about certain things once—those

things will push from you that might otherwise destroy you—and decide about other things that you will incorporate into your life, things that will bring you eternal happiness. Decide to believe in God, who created you. Decide to believe in yourself, that you truly can reach goals—your goals. Decide to work. You can be successful in any righteous endeavor when you are willing to work under the guiding hand of the Lord.

May we all make our decisions in the favorable light of the gospel of Jesus Christ, I pray in the name of Jesus Christ, amen.

A conference address from the November 1980 Ensign.

THE PRIVILEGE OF HOLDING THE PRIESTHOOD

President Spencer W. Kimball

Some years ago a young Primary boy was on a train going to California in the days when we traveled on trains. He was all alone. He sat near the window watching the telephone poles go by. Across the aisle from him was a gentleman who also was going to California. The attention of the gentleman was called to this very young boy traveling all alone without friends or relatives. He was neatly dressed and well behaved. And this gentleman was quite impressed with him.

Finally, after some time, the gentleman crossed the aisle and sat down by the young man and said to him, "Hello, young man, where are you going?"

He said, "I am going to Los Angeles."

"Do you have relatives there?"

The boy said, "I have some relatives there. I am going to visit my grandparents. They will meet me at the station, and I will stay with them a few days during the school vacation."

The next questions were "Where did you come from?" and "Where do you live?"

And the boy said, "Salt Lake City, Utah."

"Oh, then," said a gentleman, "you must be a Mormon."

And the boy said, "Yes, I am." There was pride in his voice.

The gentleman said, "Well, that's interesting. I've wondered about the Mormons and what they believe. I've been through their beautiful city; I've noticed the beautiful buildings, the tree-lined streets, the lovely homes, the beautiful rose and flower gardens, but I've never stopped to find out what makes them as they are. I wish I knew what they believe."

And the boy said to him, "Well, sir, I can tell you what they believe. 'We believe in God, the Eternal Father, and in His Son, Jesus Christ, and in the Holy Ghost' " (first article of faith).

The businessman was a bit surprised but listened intently, and the boy continued, " 'We believe that men will be punished for their own sins, and not for Adam's transgression' " (second article of faith).

And the traveling companion thought, "This is rather unusual for a mere boy to know these important things."

The boy went on: " 'We believe that through the Atonement of Christ, all mankind may be saved, by obedience to the laws and ordinances of the Gospel' " (third article of faith). And the gentleman was amazed at the knowledge and understanding of a mere boy—he was yet to be a Scout. But he continued and gave the fourth article of faith and said, " 'We believe that the first principles and ordinances of the Gospel are: first, Faith in the Lord Jesus Christ; second, Repentance; third, Baptism by immersion for the remission of sins; fourth, Laying on of hands for the gift of the Holy Ghost.' "

"That is wonderful," said the gentleman. "I am amazed that you know so well the doctrines of your church. I commend you."

With a good start and with encouragement, Johnny continued. " 'We believe that a man must be called of God, by prophecy, and by the laying on of hands by those who are in authority, to preach the gospel and administer in the ordinances thereof" (fifth article of faith).

"That's very solid doctrine, my boy," the gentleman said. "I am curious now to know how they get called of God. I can understand how they would receive the call and be established with the laying on of hands, but I wonder who has the authority to preach the gospel and administer in the ordinances thereof."

They discussed calling and sustaining and laying on of hands. Then the lad said, "Would you like to know more?"

The gentleman thought that was very unusual for a boy in these tender years to know what the Church taught, and he said, "Yes, go on."

So Johnny quoted, " 'We believe in the same organization that existed in the Primitive Church, namely, apostles, prophets, pastors, teachers, evangelists, and so forth' " (sixth article of faith).

That brought some other discussion. "You mean that your church has apostles such as James and John and Peter and Paul, and prophets such as Moses, Abraham, Isaac, and Daniel, and also evangelists?"

And the boy responded quickly, "Yes, even evangelists. We call them patriarchs, and they are appointed in all parts of the Church where there are stakes. And by inspiration they give to all the members of the Church, as required, what is called a patriarchal blessing. I have already had my patriarchal blessing, and I read it frequently. Now we have twelve apostles who have the same calling and the same authority as given to the apostles in the days of old."

The gentleman came back with these questions: "Do you speak in tongues? Do you believe in revelations and prophecies?"

And the boy brightened up as he quoted, " 'We believe in the gift of tongues, prophecy, revelation, visions, healing, interpretation of tongues, and so forth' " (seventh article of faith).

The gentleman gasped. "This sounds like you believe in the Bible!"

And the boy repeated again. "We do. 'We believe the Bible to be the word of God as far as it is translated correctly; we also believe the Book of Mormon to be the word of God' " (eighth article of faith).

The gentleman discerned that we believe both in the scriptures and in revelation. And the boy quoted, " 'We believe all that God has revealed, all that He does now reveal, and we believe that He will yet reveal many great and important things pertaining to the Kingdom of God' " (ninth article of faith). And then he continued, " 'We believe [also] in the literal gathering of Israel and in the restoration of the Ten Tribes; that Zion (the New Jerusalem) will be built upon the American continent; that Christ will reign personally upon the earth; and, that the earth will be renewed and receive its paradisiacal glory' " (tenth article of faith).

The gentleman was listening intently. He showed no interest in crossing the aisle back to his own seat. Then Johnny came in again. He said, " 'We claim the privilege of worshipping Almighty God according to the dictates of our own conscience, and allow all men the same privilege, let them worship how, where, or what they may' " (eleventh article of faith). He then continued, " 'We believe in being subject to kings, presidents, rulers, and magistrates, in obeying, honoring, and sustaining the law' " (twelfth article of faith).

And then as a final contribution, the boy repeated the thirteenth article of faith. " 'We believe in being honest, true, chaste, benevolent, virtuous, and in doing good to all men; indeed, we may say that we follow the admonition of Paul—We believe all things, we hope all things, we have endured many things, and hope to be able to endure all things. If there is anything virtuous, lovely, or of good report or praiseworthy, we seek after these things.' "

This youngster relaxed now as he finished the Articles of Faith. The gentleman was clearly excited, not only at the ability of this young boy to outline the whole program of the Church, but at the very completeness of its doctrine.

He said, "You know, after I have been to Los Angeles a couple of days, I expect to go back to New York, where my office is. I am going to wire my company that I will be a day or two late and that I am going to stop in Salt Lake City en route home and go to the information bureau there and hear all the things, in more detail, about which you have told me."

I am wondering how many of you know the Articles of Faith. How many of you big men, as well as the little men? Have you repeated them? You are always prepared with a sermon when you know the Articles of Faith. And they are basic, aren't they? I would think it would be a wonderful thing if all the boys, as they learn them, would learn them word perfect. That means that you don't miss and you don't forget.

Shall I tell you how I did it? I think I have told you before, but I used to milk cows. I typed with two fingers, and I would type out these Articles of Faith on little cards and put them down in the corral right by me when I sat on the one-legged stool and milked the cows. And I repeated them over, I guess, twenty million times. I don't know. But at any rate, I have claimed that I could say the Articles of Faith now after these many, many years and could say them word perfect. And I think it has been most valuable to me. Will you do that, my fine young men?

Now to you older men, I want to quote a few scriptures to you. Going to the book of Hebrews, written, I think, by Paul, we read:

"God, who at sundry times and in divers manners spake in time past unto the fathers by the prophets,

"Hath in these last days spoken unto us by his Son, whom he hath appointed heir of all things, by whom also he made the worlds;

"Who being the brightness of his glory, and the express image of his person, and upholding all things by the word of his power, when he had by himself purged our sins, sat down on the right hand of the Majesty on high;

"Being made so much better than the angels, as he hath by inheritance obtained a more excellent name than they" (Heb. 1:1–4).

And that reminds us of the 132nd section of the Doctrine and Covenants, where he promises that those who have received this new and everlasting covenant and who lived up to their covenants will exceed the angels. He goes beyond the gods and angels that are waiting there to guard the gates.

"For unto which of the angels said he at any time, Thou art my Son, this day have I begotten thee? And again, I will be to him a Father, and he shall be to me a Son?" (Heb. 1:5).

The heavens may be full of angels, but they are not like the Son of God, and we could add they are not like you who have qualified for this high calling to be exalted in the Lord's kingdom through the blessings that he has promised.

"And again, when he bringeth in the firstbegotten into the world, he saith, And let all the angels of God worship him" (Heb. 1:6).

That is the Son of God. That is Jesus Christ, whom we worship, with all our souls, all our minds and might and strength. He it is who is the Son of God.

"Therefore we ought to give the more earnest heed to the things which we have heard, lest at any time we should let them slip" (Heb. 2:1). *We should let them slip.* Oh, I hope as we find our way in this great program that we will never let these glorious things slip.

"How shall we escape, if we neglect so great salvation; which at the first began to be spoken by the Lord, and was confirmed unto us by them that heard him" (Heb. 2:3).

Peter, James, and John, Paul, others of the brethren—we heard this great plan of salvation from them, after they had heard it from the Lord who established it.

"For it became him, for whom are all things, and by whom are all things, in bringing many sons unto glory, to make the captain of their salvation perfect through sufferings" (Heb. 2:10).

Brethren, you may become gods. There seems to be plenty of space out there in the universe. And the Lord has proved that he knows how to do it. I think he could make, or probably have us help make, worlds for all of us, for every one of us.

Just think of the possibilities, the potential. Every little boy that has just been born becomes an heir to this glorious, glorious program. When he is grown, he meets a lovely woman; they are married in the holy temple. They live all the commandments of the Lord.

They keep themselves clean. And then they become sons of God, and they go forward with their great program—they go beyond the angels, beyond the angels and the gods that are waiting there. They go to their exaltation.

You remember in the 132nd section it says that Abraham received all that he received in this same manner, and that Abraham already was on his throne. He had his exaltation. It has been a long time since he died, of course.

For then Paul speaks again: "Forasmuch then as the children are partakers of flesh and blood, he also himself likewise took part of the same; that through death he might destroy him that had the power of death, that is, the devil" (Heb. 2:14) by being subject to death, and going into that experience, and then coming forth from the dead a resurrected being.

"For verily he took not on him the nature of angels; but he took on him the seed of Abraham" (Heb. 2:16).

And so through Abraham, Isaac, and Jacob, through David finally, the Lord became the Son of God through Abraham.

"Wherefore, holy brethren, partakers of the heavenly calling, consider the Apostle and High Priest of our profession, Christ Jesus. . . .

"For this man was counted worthy of more glory than Moses, inasmuch as he who hath builded the house hath more honour than the house. . . .

"Wherefore I was grieved with that generation [the Lord said, speaking of the people who were in Egypt and were subject to the bondage of that country]—"Wherefore I was grieved with that generation, and said, They do alway err in their heart; and they have not known my ways.

"So I sware in my wrath, They shall not enter into my rest" (Heb. 3:1, 3, 10–11).

Sometimes we have thought of rest as being a place where we get on the chaise lounge, or in our sneakers, or we get outside and lie on the grass, something where we are at rest. That isn't the kind of rest that the Lord is speaking about. It is he who is the most dynamic, the one who works the hardest, puts in the longest hours, and lives the closest to his Heavenly Father who is rested—rested from his labors, but not put away from his work.

Now I would like to give another few lines from another scripture. This one is in the Pearl of Great Price. Most of you hold the priesthood; it is a great privilege to hold the priesthood, a great privilege. And let me read to you a few lines from your father Abraham to show you how important it was to him. He says:

"And, finding there was greater happiness and peace and rest [this other kind of rest, the kind that you work at] for me, I sought for the blessings of the fathers, and the right whereunto I should be ordained to administer the same; having been myself a follower of righteousness, desiring also to be one who possessed great knowledge, and to be a greater follower of righteousness, and to possess a greater knowledge, and to be a father of many nations, a prince of peace, and desiring to receive instructions, and to keep the commandments of God, I became a rightful heir, a High Priest, holding the right belonging to the fathers" (Abr. 1:2).

It was ten generations, I believe, from Adam to Noah, and then it was ten generations, I believe, from Noah to Abraham. He inherited the blessings of the fathers.

And who are the fathers? They were the righteous men who were the patriarchs to the nations in those first years.

He says, "It was conferred upon me from the fathers; it came down from the fathers, from the beginning of time [When was that? I guess we would say when Adam was placed on the earth], yea, even from the beginning, or before the foundation of the earth, down to the present time, even the right of the firstborn, on the first man, who is Adam, our first father, through the fathers unto me.

"I sought for mine appointment unto the Priesthood according to the appointment of God unto the fathers concerning the seed" (Abr. 1:3–4).

This is something that we are heir to, we were born heir to it, and all we need to do is qualify for it to obtain this blessing, without which we never could go to the temple, we could never be sealed. And therefore, we could have no families; we could not go on with our work.

"My fathers, having turned from their righteousness, and from the holy commandments which the Lord their God had given unto them, . . . [they] utterly refused to hearken to my voice" (Abr. 1:5).

So Abraham had to leave. He left Chaldea and went north up the river until he came to Haran—what is now Turkey. And then from there to Palestine.

Now if I haven't wearied you with this reading, I should like you to read another two or three lines.

"And his voice was unto me [after the Lord struck down the man who was taking Abraham's life on the altar, "His voice came to me and he said]: . . . my name is Jehovah, and I have heard thee, and have come down to deliver thee, and to take thee away from thy father's house, and from all thy kinsfolk, into a strange land which thou knowest not of. . . .

"As it was with Noah so shall it be with thee; but through thy ministry my name shall be known in the earth forever" (Abr. 1:16, 19). And he says, "I will . . . put upon thee my name" (Abr. 1:18). *My name.* The priesthood is called the "Holy Priesthood, after the Order of the Son of God" (D&C 107:3). And then Melchizedek's name was given to the priesthood so we wouldn't repeat too often the name of the Son of God. And in connection with that, I frequently think we use the names of Deity a little too much, probably, a little too intimately, I think. There is a good example, that the Lord gave the priesthood the name of the Melchizedek Priesthood to avoid the repetition.

Now, one other thought before I close, and that is this: "I shall endeavor, hereafter," Abraham said, "to delineate the chronology running back from myself to the beginning of the creation, for the records have come into my hands, which I hold unto this present time. . . .

"But the records of the fathers, even the patriarchs, concerning the right of Priesthood, the Lord my God preserved in mine own hands; therefore a knowledge of the beginning of the creation, and also of the planets, and of the stars, as they were made known unto the fathers, have I kept even unto this day, and I shall endeavor to write some of these things upon this record, for the benefit of my posterity that shall come after me" (Abr. 1:28, 31).

Brethren, it is really something to hold the priesthood—to hold this advancing priesthood from deacon to teacher to priest—and then to hold the priesthood which is permanent, permanent as long as we are worthy of it and which can be our shield and our way unto the eternal worlds. I pray the Lord will bless us that we may never consider it a common, ordinary thing to be just an elder—"He is only an elder." "He is only a seventy." "He is only a high priest." To be a high priest, a *high priest,* is really something in the life of any man. And to consider it less than unusual and wonderful would be to not understand the blessings that have been given.

Now this comes from the doctrines we possess. The Lord has said, "I am the Almighty." "I am Jesus Christ." "I am Jehovah." He is the one we worship. We sing about him in nearly every song. We pray about him in all our prayers. We talk about him in all our meetings. We love him, and we adore him. And we promise and rededicate ourselves over and over and over that we will from this moment forth live nearer to him and to his promises and to the blessings which he has given us. I say this to you with all of our affection and love.

From the October 1978 New Era.

A MAN CALLED JOHN

Elder Bruce R. McConkie

One or twice in a thousand years, sometimes as often as every hundred years or so, always at irregular intervals, always when the divine purpose calls for such an event—a man of near divine stature comes to earth. Abraham was one; Moses another. Joseph Smith is the one for our day.

These mighty men—spiritual giants numbered with the noble and great in premortal life—always stand as beacons to the world. The work they do changes the course of history. And their lives are filled with drama and conflict. Such a man was John the Baptist.

What do we know about John the Baptist? There is enough sure knowledge to fill a book and enough speculative nonsense for a sequel. John lived and ministered and died—all in a dramatic and unusual way.

His birth was foretold by the ancient prophets; they announced him as a voice who would cry in the wilderness, preparing the way before the Lord. Gabriel himself, an angel who stands in the presence of God, came to Zacharias to tell him that his aged wife Elisabeth would soon bear a son, whose name should be John, and that he would introduce the Messiah to Israel. Zacharias was smitten both deaf and dumb until the birth and naming of his son because he questioned the word of Gabriel.

This John bore a testimony of Jesus like none other ever borne by any prophet. John bore it before his own birth and while he was yet in his mother's womb, thus fulfilling Gabriel's promise: "He shall be filled with the Holy Ghost, even from his mother's womb" (Luke 1:15).

About thirty years later John was baptizing at Bethabara. Jesus came to him and John testified: "Behold the Lamb of God, which taketh away the sin of the world" (John 1:29). And we doubt not that after he had languished for nearly a year in the foul dungeons of Machaerus and was then slain at the command of an evil Herod named Antipas, his dying words bore a like witness.

We know that John was fearless in denouncing sin, even accusing King Herod of incest and adultery. We know that Jesus sent angels to comfort him in his prison and that the Lord said that among them that are born of woman there has not been a greater prophet than John.

But the central act of his life and the one thing above all others that he did was to baptize the Son of God. As a priest of the Levitical or Aaronic order, John was calling upon men to repent and be baptized for the remission of sins. He chose Bethabara on the Jordan River as the site for his baptisms, and great hosts flocked to him to hear his doctrine and be baptized under his hands.

This preaching and these baptisms were preparing a people for the coming of the Lord. "I indeed baptize you with water unto repentance," he proclaimed, "but he that cometh after me is mightier than I, whose shoes I am not worthy to bear: he shall baptize you with the Holy Ghost, and with fire."

Then Jesus came, journeying from Galilee to the Jordan near Jerusalem. He asked for baptism. In awe, overwhelmed that the very Son of God himself should seek baptism at his hand, and yet knowing before that such would be the case, John said: "I have need to be baptized of thee, and comest thou to me?" Jesus replied: "Suffer it to be so now: for thus it becometh us to fulfill all righteousness."

John acceded to his cousin's wish. Solemnly, with dignity, in the power and authority of the priesthood of Aaron—by which authority the Levites had baptized through the centuries—he immersed the Lord Jesus in the murky waters of the Jordan.

Then came the miracle—the heavens were opened and John saw the Holy Ghost descending in peace and serenity, like a dove, to be and abide with the Lamb of God forever. This is one of possibly two occasions in all history, of which we have record, in which the personage of the Holy Ghost was seen by mortal man. And yet there was more to come. A voice spoke, a voice from heaven, the voice of the Father of us all. It said in words of glorious majesty: "This is my beloved Son, in whom I am well pleased." (See Matt. 3:11–17.)

This in brief is the biblical story of John, and to every story in the scriptures there is a moral, a teaching, a doctrine— something that will guide and help those of us who read the scriptures and ponder their deep and marvelous meanings. What we are to learn from the baptism of Jesus was expressed by Nephi in these words: "And now, if the Lamb of God, he being holy"—and truly Christ was without sin—"should have need to be baptized by water, to fulfill all righteousness, O then, how much more need have we, being unholy"—and who among us has not sinned—"to be baptized, yea, even by water!"

Christ was not baptized for the remission of sins because he had none. But, as Nephi recounts, he was baptized for the following reasons: (1) As a token of humility before the Father; (2) As a covenant that he would keep the commandments; (3) As a prelude to receiving the gift of the Holy Ghost; (4) To gain entrance to and be saved in the kingdom of God, for no one, not even the Son of God, can so obtain without baptism; and (5) As a pattern and an example for all men, and so that he could say: "Follow thou me" and also, "He that is baptized in my name, to him will the Father give the Holy Ghost, like unto me; wherefore, follow me, and do the things which ye have seen me do." (See 2 Ne. 31:5-12.)

And finally, for us in these last days, perhaps the most wondrous thing in the life of John is that he came, in resurrected glory, to Joseph Smith and Oliver Cowdery, on the 15th day of May in 1829. To them he said: "Upon you my fellow servants, in the name of Messiah I confer the Priesthood of Aaron, which holds the keys of the ministering of angels, and of the gospel of repentance, and of baptism by immersion for the remission of sins; and this shall never be taken again from the earth, until the sons of Levi do offer again an offering unto the Lord in righteousness" (D&C 13).

The Lord be praised for the life and ministry of a man called John.

From the May 1984 New Era.

DEACON

THE ROLE OF THE DEACON

Elder Vaughn J. Featherstone

Several years ago I heard a story that I shall not soon forget:
A young man, climbing in some rugged, high mountain
peaks, came across an eagle's nest. The nest contained several
eggs. He took one and gently carried it back to his home. He
then put it with several eggs an old hen was setting over. In due
time all of the eggs were hatched, and there came forth the
eaglet with the baby chicks. During the next several months the
baby eagle grew along with the chicks. He scratched in the
barnyard for his food like chickens do. Although he grew to full
size, he still never flew. The young man watched the process
with great interest. He wanted the eagle to fly. So one day he
took the eagle up on top of his house and said, "Thou art an
eagle, fly." But the eagle just flew down to the barnyard and
commenced scratching like the chickens. A few days later, long
before sunlight, the young lad took the eagle to a lofty crag high
among the mountain peaks. Then, as the first streaks of sunlight
burst over the mountain range, he said, "Thou art an eagle, fly."
The eagle began to stretch its wings; its eye caught a shaft of
sunlight; a sensation swept through it from wing tip to wing tip.
The fresh, cool air, the smell of pine trees, and an exhilaration
it had never known coursed through the great bird. Its wings
spread wider; power swept through its entire frame. It began to
lift off the arm of the young man. Soon it was lifting and soaring
hundreds of feet above the high peaks. It lifted higher and

higher and soared farther and farther into the endless sky. It saw more in an instant than its earthbound chicken companions saw in a lifetime. From that time forth the eagle was never more content to be a barnyard fowl.

Once a deacon has felt the power and exhilaration of truly magnifying his priesthood and lifting to the endless bounds of service, he too will no longer be content to be a barnyard fowl, an ordinary boy. He will want to represent God on the earth and be one of his holy and choice servants.

A deacon "is to be ordained according to the gifts and callings of God unto him; and he is to be ordained by the power of the Holy Ghost, which is in the one who ordains him" (D&C 20:60). "No person is to be ordained to any office in this church, where there is a regularly organized branch of the same, without the vote of that church" (D&C 20:65).

A deacon's duties include passing the sacrament, visiting homes of members and receiving fast offerings, providing messenger service for the bishop and his counselors, and home teaching as a junior companion when there are not sufficient priests and teachers. These responsibilities are commonly known by almost every deacon.

The deacon also has other responsibilities that are a little more subtle but vitally important.

Dress standards: Every deacon is expected to be appropriately attired as he performs his duty. When passing the sacrament he should be dressed conservatively with a dress shirt and tie. Loud or gaudy patterns of dress attract the attention of the Saints and take their minds off the sacred sacramental service. No young man would deliberately violate his priesthood ordination by causing this distraction. His hair length should be such that it does not give a feminine appearance or distract members' concentration.

When a young man is a messenger for the bishop he should be neat and clean in appearance and be one in whom the bishop could feel justifiable pride. As the deacon visits the homes of members he should be neatly dressed to function in his priesthood assignment. In some few cases the only contact inactive members have with the Church is the monthly visit of a deacon to receive a fast offering contribution. That brief visit may have a powerful influence on our inactive members. Deacons should be neat and clean and their conduct should be dignified with warmth and friendliness. A genuine smile and firm handshake by a young deacon might well cause serious reflections by inactive members. A home teaching assignment ought to be carried out in the same dignified manner. A deacon should always be prepared to bear his testimony to a family should his senior companion invite it.

Conduct: A deacon must conduct himself properly in all things. This is, however, especially true in his conduct at the sacrament table. We have all seen immature deacons who play, make faces, laugh, push other deacons, and in general are very light-minded about this sacred ordinance. Such a young man should be taught that he is violating the sacred trust that the Lord has given him to assist in the ordinance. A deacon should conduct himself following a single standard. We do not have a double standard in the Church. A deacon should refrain from telling dirty stories, reading pornographic material, using profane language, or being abusive or rude. It takes maturity to live the standards, and those deacons who do will find success in the world and great opportunities for service in God's kingdom.

Worthiness: All of our priesthood assignments should be determined by our worthiness. A deacon should be honest in all of his dealings. The truth must be part of his conduct and expression. Never would he violate this by lying or cheating at home, school, or a place of entertainment. A deacon must be morally clean and pure in thought. He would never violate the Word of Wisdom or be involved in drug abuse. His concern should be to prove himself worthy every day of his life. As he does, growth, development, and success will be his. One of the greatest goals we can have as individuals is to become pure in heart. As we faithfully strive to live worthily, we become pure in heart.

Service: Many years ago I attended a conference with President Marion G. Romney. During the break between sessions of conference, we went for a short walk. One of the things he said to me was, "Brother Featherstone, do you think the brethren of the priesthood will ever come to understand that they were born to serve their fellowmen?" In one sentence he gave me a concept that has been a great motivating factor in my life. I commend it to you.

I earnestly pray that every deacon will come to understand that he was born to serve his fellowmen.

From the May 1974 New Era.

"THEY WERE AWESOME!"

Elder Robert L. Backman

On a trip to the Orient it was my privilege to attend a sacrament meeting of the Naha Branch on the island of Okinawa. I was so impressed with the quality of the sacrament service and the reverence and dignity exhibited by the Aaronic Priesthood that when I was called to speak I asked one of the young men to join me at the pulpit. I asked him, "How do you feel knowing you hold the priesthood of God?" Not tall enough to see over the pulpit, he raised on his toes so he could see the congregation, then with deep emotion responded: "It's the greatest honor of my life!"

Some of us, because we receive the Aaronic Priesthood when we are very young, do not appreciate what an honor it is for us to be singled out from all of God's sons to represent him with this sacred power and authority. Have you ever wondered what it would have been like to be with Joseph Smith and Oliver Cowdery on the banks of the Susquehanna River on that spring day, May 15, 1829? Can you picture the miracle and majesty of that moment when John the Baptist, a resurrected being, appeared to those two young men, laid his hands on their heads, and granted them the authority of the Aaronic Priesthood?

Oliver Cowdery captured that unforgettable experience in his personal account. I hope you can feel the wonder and joy they felt as you read his words:

"On a sudden, as from the midst of eternity, the voice of the

Redeemer spake peace to us, while the veil was parted and the angel of God came down clothed with glory and delivered the anxiously looked for message, and the keys of the Gospel of repentance. What joy! what wonder! what amazement! While the world was racked and distracted—while millions were groping as the blind for the wall, and while all men were resting upon uncertainty, as a general mass, our eyes beheld—our ears heard. As in the 'blaze of day'; yes, more—above the glitter of the May sunbeam, which then shed its brilliancy over the face of nature! Then his voice, though mild, pierced to the center, and his words, 'I am thy fellow-servant,' dispelled every fear. We listened, we gazed, we admired! 'Twas the voice of an angel from glory—'twas a message from the Most High, and as we heard we rejoiced, while His love enkindled upon our souls, and we were rapt in the vision of the Almighty! Where was room for doubt? Nowhere; uncertainty had fled, doubt had sunk, no more to rise, while fiction and deception had fled forever. . . .

"I shall not attempt to paint to you the feelings of this heart, nor the majestic beauty and glory which surrounded us on this occasion; but you will believe me when I say, that earth, nor men, with the eloquence of time, cannot begin to clothe language in as interesting and sublime a manner as this holy personage. No; nor has this earth power to give the joy, to bestow the peace, or comprehend the wisdom which was contained in each sentence as it was delivered by the power of the Holy Spirit! Man may deceive his fellow man; deception may follow deception, and the children of the wicked one may have power to seduce the foolish and untaught, till naught but fiction feeds the many, and the fruit of falsehood carries in its current the giddy to the grave, but one touch with the finger of his love, yes, one ray of glory from the upper world, or one word from the mouth of the Savior, from the bosom of eternity, strikes it all into insignificance, and blots it forever from the mind! The assurance that we were in the presence of an angel; the certainty that we heard the voice of Jesus, and the truth unsullied as it flowed from a pure personage, dictated by the will of God, is to me, past description, and I shall ever look upon this expression of the Savior's goodness with wonder and thanksgiving while I am permitted to tarry, and in those mansions where perfection dwells and sin never comes, I hope to adore in that day which shall never cease" (*History of the Church* 1:43).

I tingle when I read of such a glorious occasion so vitally important in the restoration of the gospel of Jesus Christ, and I marvel when I consider the meaning of the ordination that occurred that day.

Explaining that he acted under the direction of Peter, James, and John, the ancient Apostles who held the keys of the Melchizedek Priesthood, John pronounced these words to Joseph and Oliver, who had called upon God for guidance and direction:

"Upon you my fellow servants, in the name of Messiah I confer the Priesthood of Aaron, which holds the keys of the ministering of angels, and of the gospel of repentance, and of baptism by immersion for the remission of sins; and this shall never be taken again from the earth, until the sons of Levi do offer again an offering unto the Lord in righteousness" (D&C 13).

What an awesome experience!

Although we did not share that glorious event, when we are ordained to the Aaronic Priesthood we receive the same authority and powers that John the Baptist conferred upon Joseph Smith and Oliver Cowdery. This priesthood holds the keys to significant blessings that are essential to the accomplishment of the Lord's work. That should make you stand in awe of yourself!

Let us consider the keys conferred with the priesthood of Aaron.

The first key committed by John was the key of the ministering of angels.

What does it mean to you to be in a position to have angels minister unto you? It means that you are entitled to have inspiration and guidance in all phases of your life—at home, school, work, play, as well as in church. Even on the football field—if you are honoring your priesthood.

It provides protection to you from evil and danger.

Have you read the account of Elisha and his young servant, who saw their city surrounded by the mighty army of Syria? Fearful that they would be conquered, the servant appealed to his master: "Alas, my master! how shall we do?"

The response of Elisha suggests what protection is given with the key of the ministering of angels:

"And he answered, Fear not: for they that be with us are more than they that be with them.

"And Elisha prayed, and said, Lord, I pray thee, open his eyes, that he may see. And the Lord opened the eyes of the young man; and he saw: and, behold, the mountain was full of horses and chariots of fire round about Elisha" (2 Kings 6:15–17).

It seems to me that the ministering of angels is a pretty powerful blessing to enjoy as a young man. I pray you will recognize that it is.

The second key was that of the gospel of repentance.

You may not appreciate this great saving key now, but you will. Only Jesus Christ has made it through this life without committing sin. Without the principle of repentance, all would be lost. Believe me, you will be grateful that God granted this beautiful key when he restored the gospel of Jesus Christ and named repentance only after faith in the Lord Jesus Christ among the first principles of the gospel. Think of the trust God has placed in his young sons in granting the responsibility and authority to preach repentance to his deacons, teachers, and priests.

The third key was that of baptism by immersion for the remission of sins.

When ordained to the office of priest you are granted the authority to baptize.

Of all the experiences I enjoyed as a mission president, one of the most exciting was the glorious sight of seeing the missionaries baptize converts to the Church. To see those handsome young men lead the baptismal candidates into the water to perform that sacred ordinance always brought a lump to my throat and sent a thrill up my spine. The elders felt the same way about that privilege. One of my fine missionaries had been a very adventurous lad. He loved to rappel cliffs, hang glide, and parachute jump. He even joined an Army reserve unit which gave him regular opportunities to jump. When I asked him how he felt when he stood in the baptismal font with a convert, he replied: "It's as exciting as jumping out of an airplane."

Do you appreciate what it means to possess the authority to act for God, to be his trusted son, to have the unique power of the priesthood?

When I was a boy I remember one of our Apostles and noted senators, Reed Smoot, saying: "I would rather be a deacon in The Church of Jesus Christ of Latter-day Saints than be president of the United States."

Although your duties are defined as temporal, there is nothing more spiritual than your sacred calling. In fact, the two ordinances most directly related to the atonement of Jesus Christ are Aaronic Priesthood ordinances—the sacrament and baptism.

You are entitled to be sustained by the Lord and to have his sacred power manifest through you.

I have been reading of the tremendous missionary experiences of Wilford Woodruff, some occurring while he was still a priest in the Aaronic Priesthood. His testimony should be pondered by every Aaronic Priesthood holder. It will help you understand the magnificent power God has given you.

"I traveled thousands of miles and preached the Gospel as a Priest, and . . . the Lord sustained me and made manifest His power in the defense of my life as much while I held that office as He had done while I have held the office of an Apostle. The Lord sustains any man that holds a portion of the Priesthood, whether he is a Priest, an Elder, a Seventy, or an Apostle, if he magnifies his calling and does his duty" ("Obtain the Spirit of God," *Millennial Star*, 28 Sept. 1905, p. 610).

This sacred priesthood gives you the privilege to render significant service to your fellowmen, to feel a sense of brotherhood which few of your peers enjoy, to reach out to one another as you teach your fellow priesthood holders the duties of your special calling.

As the President of the Young Men of the Church, I delight in the story of a fine deacons quorum presidency who sensed the importance of their office in teaching their quorum members.

On a recent Sunday, Mark was ordained a deacon.

When his family returned from Church, the telephone rang. It was the deacons quorum president asking for an appointment for the presidency to visit with Mark and his parents. The appointment was set for Tuesday night at 7:30 P.M. Promptly at 7:30 on Tuesday, the doorbell rang. The members of the presidency stood on the porch, dressed in suits, white shirts, and ties, each one carrying his scriptures.

Sitting down with Mark and his parents, they began with prayer, then handed an agenda to everyone there.

The quorum president then opened the scriptures, having Mark and his father read those references which speak of the power of the Aaronic Priesthood, what it is, and the particular duties of a deacon.

He then spoke about Mark's specific responsibilities and duties, explaining how he should dress as he performed his priesthood duties, where he should be to pass the sacrament, and his duties as a messenger for the bishop. He acquainted Mark with fast offering collection procedures and assured him that a counselor in the presidency would accompany him the first time. Then he asked Mark if he had any questions about his new calling.

At the end of the visit, the deacons presidency welcomed Mark into the quorum and offered help whenever he needed it. As they left, Mark's eyes were as big as saucers as he contemplated the seriousness and honor of his calling. He said to his dad: "They were awesome!"

Through the experiences of the Aaronic Priesthood quorum, you learn to accept responsibility, to be dependable and trustworthy, to do your duty. When I asked a fine deacon what he did, he replied: "I do what I am supposed to do!"

At the Scout encampment held at a beautiful site near Flagstaff, Arizona in 1982, 1,150 Eagle Scouts met in a special dinner in honor of their achievement. During the program they were asked, "How many of you are planning to serve a mission?" Every young man rose to his feet, committing himself to fulfill the responsibility President Kimball has asked the Aaronic Priesthood to prepare for. Those Aaronic Priesthood brethren knew their duty.

Above all, the Aaronic Priesthood teaches you what real happiness is. Not in acquiring possessions, wealth, position; not in giving in to the gang, appetites or passions, or to any other of Satan's temptations, but in rendering service to your fellowmen, really learning to love as our Savior taught us to love.

I know of a quorum of priests who really demonstrated how to love. Included in the quorum was a young man whose life was lived in a wheelchair because of paralysis. It was even difficult for him to speak so he could be understood. Despite his severe handicaps, the quorum rallied around him as his brothers in the gospel. They included him in all their activities. When they played basketball Eddy was there in his wheelchair, cheering them on. When they went waterskiing, Eddy was there on the bank, enjoying the outing with them. When they went to a movie, they wheeled Eddy into the theater with them. Those quorum members lifted him and his wheelchair in and out of the car wherever they went. He was truly one of them. You should have seen the bond of love that developed in that quorum. They brought happiness into their own lives. I was very proud of these young men. They honored their priesthood.

When I see hundreds of thousands of stalwart young men, sons of God, embarking on the adventure of life armed with God's holy priesthood, serving so faithfully in your wards and branches, developing testimonies of the gospel in your youth, I know that the future of the Church is secure. With the Aaronic Priesthood as a schoolmaster to assist you in coming to know your Savior, to love him and his gospel, and to prepare you to receive the sacred oath and covenant of the Melchizedek Priesthood, you fit the description of your royal generation of which we sing in that mighty hymn "Hope of Israel":

Hope of Israel, Zion's army,
Children of the promised day,
See, the chieftain signals onward,
And the battle's in array!
Hope of Israel, rise in might
With the sword of truth and right;
Sound the war-cry, "Watch and pray!"
Vanquish every foe today.
(*Hymns,* 1985, no. 259.)

From the May 1983 New Era.

THE CARE OF DEACONS

Jim Rasband

The Savior wants us to love one another. In John, chapter 13, verse 34, He said: "A new commandment I give unto you, That ye love one another; as I have loved you, that ye also love one another."

Those of us who hold offices in the Aaronic Priesthood have a special mission to live this commandment. We must pass on the Savior's love to our fellow quorum members.

Trying to get deacons active will not work if we are not living this commandment. We can visit their homes, make special parties for them, and hassle them on the phone every week. But if we only care about the quorum records or about the mechanics of our job, we won't succeed. We have to care about the inactive boy himself. His eternal life must be important to us. We must literally love him as we have been loved by the Savior, the kind of love that the Lord expressed when he said, "This is my work and my glory—to bring to pass the immortality and eternal life of man" (Moses 1:39).

So that's the first step in getting deacons active. Care. Care enough to find out what they like to do, what problems they have that you can help with. Show them that you're their friend whether they come to church or not, all the time planning things that will interest them. You've got to be willing to make a guy feel like he's part of your group, even if that means going out of your way.

When boys start feeling that you really care, care about them more than the program, they'll want to be friends with you and do what you do—be a part of what you are, namely, the deacons quorum. And then the hard part starts: you've got to keep them there. You get them there by loving them. But you've got to keep them there by having the kind of program boys like. This is where we especially need our advisers and Aaronic Priesthood directors.

Boys like to be busy. They like to improve themselves. They like sports, not just games, but organized, competitive sports. They like Scouting and the sense of achievement that it brings. We need men who care and will work with us to get merit badges and to organize activities. I guess you could say that you keep them there by loving them too. It takes a lot of caring for adults to give us that much time and interest.

In our ward we have had some success with two boys who had been completely inactive. We made friends with them. We took them out for pizza. We planned activities around their special interests. When we told them how much the program had to offer and showed them we really wanted them with us, they decided to give us a try.

Last week they both came to activity night. If we can care enough to make good on our campaign promises and really deliver the good program we've promised, and still care about them just as much, we'll keep these boys, and they will have a chance to work out their salvation.

The inactives need the active deacons to care about them. And we all need the adults to care about us. In return we can offer a great deal. We offer gratitude and admiration for the rest of our lives, and a better world in the future, because it will include the better men you have helped to build.

It is my prayer that we can all live this special commandment to love one another, in the name of Jesus Christ, amen.

From the February 1976 New Era. *Originally a talk given by twelve-year-old Jim Rasband at the Monterey California Stake conference on September 21, 1975.*

DEACON POWER

William G. Hartley

Who, besides recording angels, could count the exact number of deacons who have served the Church since Titus Billings, Serenes Burnett, and John Burk were the first deacons ordained in the Restored Church in 1830–31.

With pocket calculator in hand, we might try some rough figuring, based on annual totals (95 deacons in 1854; 18,000 in 1906; about 150,000 in 1975) and turnover rates (two or three years service per deacon), to conservatively estimate more than two million deacons. The Lord must assign great importance to the office to have called so many deacons to serve in his kingdom in the last days.

Warm Recollections of Days as Deacons

Many leading men in the Church have gone on record as being impressed with the power of deacons and as having warm memories of their own days as deacons. To cite a century-old example, John Smith, an English convert, recalled as a mature man that "he joined the Church when eleven years of age, was ordained a deacon when fifteen [1851], felt such a power as he had never felt before." Nearer to our own century, Elder George Reynolds, one of the seven presidents of the First Council of Seventy, expressed similar gratitude for his brief service as a deacon:

"If there was any duty to which I have been called in the

Church that I performed to the utmost of my ability, it was in magnifying the calling of a Deacon.

"I was never absent from meeting when it was possible for me to be there. I was often at the meeting house an hour or more before the time set for the services, to open the door and prepare the room, and I took great pleasure in seeing that everything was properly arranged—that the seats were dusted, the gas lighted in the evening, and all the other little matters attended to that made the room comfortable for the Saints to assemble in. I really believe I took more pleasure and satisfaction in that work than in the higher responsibilities of later years."

A more recent example, former Eastern States Mission President James H. Moyle, writing in the 1940s, pointed out how his call to be a deacon actually changed his boyhood behavior. When called by his bishop to be a deacon, young James, who had been hanging around with the rougher boys in the ward, hesitated briefly and then accepted:

"I gradually broke away from the roughs, and so devoted myself to the duties of deacon that the bishop said I was the best in the ward. We cleaned out the meetinghouse, swept, mopped, and dusted, filled the coal-oil lamps, trimmed the wicks, made the fire, did all the janitorial work, and put the house in order generally, and looked after the door and entrance. . . . We took our turns cleaning the meetinghouse and had to do it frequently. I was very conscientious about it, and never thereafter allowed myself to be wayward or irreligious."

Why is it, we might ask in light of these three cases, that older men have fond memories of their service as deacons? At least three solid reasons for such feelings seem apparent when we look at the history of deacons' work in this dispensation: fellowship, service, and personal development.

Fellowship

As Elder Moyle noted, a boy's standards determine those with whom he associates. Once a boy is involved in a deacons quorum, his fellow quorum members often become his best friends. They then mutually influence each other for good, as illustrated by this story:

William Smart as a youth joined his playmates in regularly upsetting a crotchety widow in their neighborhood. Then one day the boys were ordained as deacons.

"The spirit of the Deacon coming over me to some extent," said Brother Smart, "I found myself willing, and even pleased to unite with my young brother deacons in chopping wood for the poor and for the meetinghouse."

One day, seeking some fun, the deacons paused before the widow's property and discussed ways in which they might best torment the old lady. But this time the result was different.

"Since they last met here," Brother Smart recalled, "a change had crept almost imperceptibly into the lives of some of these boys. They were now Deacons in the Holy Priesthood."

Instead of pranks, one boy suggested they take the woman's wagon, pull it down the hill, load it up with dry willows, and then take the load back and chop the willows up for her woodpile. The other boys, once they realized their friend was not joking, heartily agreed.

The widow spotted the boys taking her wagon down the hill and hurled verbal arrows at them. Then she stormed to a neighbor's and vented her anger. But was she ever surprised when the old wagon was returned to her loaded with dry willows and the crew of grimy, perspiring boys—whom she recognized as her old tormentors—energetically began chopping kindling for her! She scolded, laughed, and cried alternately, then exclaimed: "Boys, God bless you! I forgive you for all your past mischief to me!" She and the boys then knew that "some silent force had wrought a change," and that invisible force was the new power and spirit they had received with their ordination.

Service

Deacons, never in Church history content to just hold meetings, have always performed important Church assignments. As assistants to teachers, priests, and bishops, they have tackled a variety of useful tasks. A century ago, for example, their primary assignment was to care for the ward meetinghouses.

"A good deal depends on a deacon in making a meeting comfortable," said deacon Mark Lindsay in 1874. "We should be there at least an hour before meeting begins. Have the house nice and clean, not too hot, nor too cold. . . . Have your sacrament plate clean, a clean table and cloth, and take care to keep it clean, or it [cloth] will be soon washed away."

Concern for the poor likewise has characterized the deacon's activities, particularly their collecting of fast offerings. Today deacons walk their fast offering routes or have older boys or fathers drive them around while they collect cash or checks in the special envelopes. Old-time deacons, by contrast, had perhaps a bit more adventure in collecting fast offerings. Borrowing a father's wagon and team, a pair of deacons would circle an assigned block, knock at each house door, and return to the wagon loaded with boxes, baskets, jars, or packages—rarely money. Two Provo deacons, for example, on a monthly fast offering trip in 1903 loaded into their wagon "2 lbs. bacon, 40¢ cash, 1 bottle fruit, 1 pk raisins, 1 can oister [sic] and 43 lbs. flour."

In addition to collecting offerings, deacons have helped the needy by donating muscle power: painting houses, raking leaves, shoveling walks, running errands. Illustrative is a case that took place near the turn of the century when deacons aided two families in their ward:

"On the tenth of May, the Deacon's quorum, with the consent of the Bishopric, assembled at the beet field of Sister _____ , whose husband had recently died. The quorum with the aid of relatives, to the number of sixty-eight, went to work, and they cultivated and thinned nine acres of beets before they quit the field. This work lifted a heavy load off the family of Sister _____ , who was in great distress at the time.

"A few days later, the Deacons went to the farm of Sister _____ , widow, and thinned several acres of beets for her also."

While a few bishops asked their deacons to pass the sacrament as early as the 1870s, it was not until after the turn of the century that passing the sacrament became a Churchwide assignment for deacons. It is included as one item in an interesting list of recommended duties for deacons published by the Church about the time of World War I:

Collect fast offerings
Messenger for bishops
Pass sacrament
Prepare fuel for widows and old people
Care for the poor
Pass out notices
Pump organ at meetings
Keep Church property in good condition
Assist in caring for cemeteries
Keep order in meetinghouse
Maintain meetinghouse grounds
Assist in Primary work
Assist in Religion Class work

Act as ushers
Boy Scout work
Attend the doors
Distribute special notices

Personal Development

Certainly through fellowship and service deacons past and present have learned important behavior patterns, attitudes, and concepts about their religion. Stewardship, the basic principle of Church government, is learned early by deacons who, given an assignment, must carry it out and report their success to their leader. Also learned are feelings of compassion when helping the needy, attitudes of worship and reverence while passing the sacrament, and respect for bishops and Church authorities while doing tasks for them.

In addition, deacons receive formal gospel education at their quorum meetings. Before the day of Church lesson manuals it was left up to the deacons themselves to decide how to spend their meetings profitably. And the old record books indicate they did a pretty good job in planning and carrying out worthwhile quorum meetings. A century ago, for example, a typical deacons' meeting involved the usual opening song, prayer, and minutes, then a mixture of moral stories like "How Rob Saved His Bacon," readings like "The First Drink," and songs like "Stay on the Farm" or "Paddle Your Own Canoe," interspersed with gospel talks and songs and frequent bearing of testimonies. Here, to cite an old minute book from Centerville, Utah, is a pre-Christmas deacons' meeting in 1884:

"Chas. Tingey commenced by Reading the 5th chap. of Daniel. Which was a description of the writing on the wall concerning the destruction of the Kingdom of Beltschazzer. Perry Tingey read a selection Entitled 'A Little Girl's Xmas Thoughts.' Jn. Capner lectured a few minutes on the 12th Chapter of Isaiah. He concluded his remarks by reading the Chapter. Samuel Capner spoke upon the order that should be observed in our meetings. P G Tingey, James Smith, Parley Parrish, Harry Barber, and Wm Miller each spoke a few minutes. Roll Called. Programme for the next meeting read."

While somewhat casual and unsystematic, such quorum meetings produced meaningful gospel understanding as well as practical public speaking and singing experience.

Only after 1908 did deacons quorums receive systematic courses of study to use in their meetings, and over the years since then the Presiding Bishopric has provided scores of carefully prepared courses and different lesson manuals geared to teach deacons both religious principles and righteous conduct—gospel theory and application.

Because of these three characteristics of deacons' work—fellowship, service, and personal development—older men, who have served long in priesthood work, look back gratefully to the time when they stepped onto the beginning rung of the priesthood ladder to serve as deacons.

A Crippled Church without Deacons

Not horsepower but priesthood power moves the Church forward, and deacon power is an essential part. Without deacon power, the Church would suffer in two ways. First, bishops and others would have to drop some of their own duties in order to take upon themselves the work that deacons are supposed to do. Second, and perhaps most important, if a generation of deacons fail, within two years there would be no teachers, in four years no priests, and after a decade or two the ranks of the Melchizedek Priesthood quorums would not be filled with the prepared and qualified adults, graduates of the preparatory Aaronic Priesthood.

Brigham Young's generation described deacons and other Aaronic Priesthood members as being the legs and feet of the Church, without which the Church would be crippled. But it is also important to note that without Aaronic Priesthood experience, boys themselves would be crippled. So deacon power involves both benefit to the Church and benefit to the deacon.

Two million deacons. That's a lot of fellowship, a lot of service to the Church, a lot of personal development. And when we get right down to it, these qualities—and not statistics—are what recording angels and our Heavenly Father are most concerned about.

From the May 1975 New Era.

ON WATER AND BREAD

Laird Roberts

It was one of the first warm days of early spring. The windows of our church were open for the first time that year, and bright, warm sunlight spilled in long rays into the chapel. A small, spring wind came through the windows carrying the fragrances of unseen blossoms. My grandparents and several aunts and uncles were sitting proudly with my parents. I was sitting on the front row of the chapel with the deacons. It was my first time passing the sacrament.

The sacrament song ended.

The bishop nodded to us, and in a single motion we stood and walked to the table. The white cloth had been removed and carefully folded, and then the prayer was spoken. I felt the importance of the words and the ordinance as I never had before. With my relatives and what seemed like the entire congregation watching me, I tried to move with as much reverence and dignity as I could. I felt a strong feeling of pride to be able to pass the sacrament. It was a great honor. When the meeting was over, nearly everyone in my ward congratulated me.

Several months passed, and in that time, along with the other members of my quorum, I began to forget, a little, the honor of holding the priesthood and of passing the sacrament. We stopped remembering what the ordinance stood for. It became a chore. Something we had to do. A job we were given because no one else wanted to do it.

This attitude began to affect the way we performed the ordinance. They were small differences. We were sometimes late for sacrament meeting. Occasionally we didn't dress as appropriately as we should have. And we talked during the meeting, not loudly and not during the sacrament service, but enough that it was noticed. They were small things, but they took away from the sacredness of the ordinance we were charged with.

The bishop asked our adviser to talk to us about it. Every Sunday morning for weeks he tried to explain to us the importance of what we were doing, of the priesthood of God, and of the ordinance of the sacrament. He told us of the sons of Aaron, of Gethsemane, and Calvary. He was an older man, and we could tell he felt strongly about the things he was telling us. We would straighten up a little. Then a few Sundays would pass, and we would slip back again.

One Sunday after our priesthood class had ended, our adviser stopped us.

"You don't have to worry about the sacrament today," he said. "It's been taken care of."

We were surprised and curious, but we were also glad to get out of the job, even if it was just for one day. We came into the meeting late as usual, during the song, and sat on a middle row. Sitting on the deacons bench with our adviser were the high priests of our ward. They were the oldest and most respected men in our ward. Two of them had been bishops, one a stake president. All had held positions of honor and leadership. The song ended. They rose, and the prayer was said.

By their bearing and by their reverence it was easy to see they felt great respect and honor for what they were doing. It was no menial task for them. They were all dressed in dark suits, white shirts, and ties. But it was more than the way they were dressed or even the way they carried themselves in performing the ordinance. The congregation was silent. The sacrament became something deeply felt and sacred. There was something deeper, something much more significant. There was a spirit to it. A feeling deeper than words.

The windows in the chapel were open that Sunday. It was late fall, and the fragrance of fall came in through the windows. I could see patches of a blue sky. Leaves were falling from the trees. I was humbled. Passing the sacrament wasn't a job no one else wanted. It was a job I had been given as a sacred trust. It was the greatest of honors.

From the May 1984 New Era.

MY BROTHER

Kirk Sheldon Wilkinson

There isn't a day that goes by that I don't thank the Lord for my brother who saved my life. I can remember that terrible day as if it were yesterday. I love my brother and would do anything to pay him back. I was quite young at the time, but the impact that this experience had on my life will be eternal.

It was a bright, sunny Saturday early in June. We lived in the city in a typical neighborhood—a lot of kids and a lot of cars. That morning while my brother was mowing the lawn, I was playing in the driveway with my friend Jeff, who lived two houses down. Jeff was my best friend, and we were having a great time seeing who could hit the baseball past the other person. Jay, my older brother, was like no other brother in the whole world. He watched after me and was always willing to help me, even with little problems that seemed important to me. He was my example of true brotherly love. He took me everywhere; we were inseparable. Even though he was many years older than I was, I could tell he was as proud of me and I was of him. I loved my big brother, and I know he loved me.

Jeff and I were still playing hard as Jay finished mowing the lawn directly in front of the house and began to mow the small patch of grass that separated the sidewalk from the street. I admired the way Jay worked, especially when he worked hard. He was my example of what I wanted to be. Suddenly the lawn mower stopped. I guessed he hit a rock with the blade and it caused the motor to stall. I turned to see if he needed help to restart it. As I turned to Jay, Jeff let go with a throw that made me look silly. The ball zoomed out into the street, and I ran after it, not noticing the speeding truck that was coming right for me. Evidently Jay saw the truck and came running into the street after me. I never did see the truck but felt a powerful push causing me to be hurled to the other side of the street. As I fell to the ground, I could hear the sound of screeching brakes and a thud accompanied by a painful groan. My heart sank into my stomach as I picked myself up off the ground and ran over to Jay who was lying halfway under the truck that had hit him. With tears in my eyes I sat down next to him and put my arms tightly around him in a way that only a little brother can.

"Jay, please wake up! Jay, please wake up!" I pleaded with all my heart through the tears. "Jay, please wake up!" I loved my big brother.

Soon Mom came running out of the house to see what had happened. Seeing her son on the ground, she burst into tears. She slowly bent down and put her arms around Jay, and together in the middle of the street we shared tears over the one we loved. I could hear sirens in the distance; they were going to take my big brother away. That only made me tighten my arms and cry harder. Jay was limp and becoming cold. I was scared and didn't want to leave my brother. Dad got home from work just as the ambulance arrived, and Mom got up and ran to him. Dad came running over to Jay with tears in his eyes. He motioned to me to let go so that they could lift Jay into the ambulance. As I got up, I leaned over and whispered in Jay's ear, "I love you, Jay. Please come home."

The drivers closed the back doors of the ambulance after Dad got in with Jay, and they began to drive off down the street. The siren was so loud and seemed to hurt as Mom picked me up in her arms. Crying together we went into the house. Mom set me down and went up to her room to be alone. She was crying harder than I'd ever seen her cry before. I, too, cried and cried hard. Even as I went to my room and knelt down to pray, the tears still streamed down my face. I took a deep breath and began to pray through the gasps of tears, "Father in Heaven, please help Jay be well. Don't let him die. I love Jay. Please don't let him die!"

My tears still flowed as Mom came downstairs and slowly opened my door. She was trying hard not to cry. There was a moment of silence while she looked at me with greater love and greater sorrow than ever before. A moment passed, and then she ran over to me, picked me up in her arms, and through newly formed tears she whispered in my ear, "Kirk, I love you." We cried together for hours.

Dad didn't come home that night; neither did Jay. I never saw my big brother again after I held him in my arms as he lay cold and limp in the street. I was alive and Jay was dead. What had I done to deserve to live? His life was so much better than mine. My brother died for me! He died so that I could live. He saved my life.

Many years have passed since Jay pushed me out of the way of that truck. My life was changed in a matter of minutes, and I have taken it upon myself to tell the world what my brother did to save my life. I have tried to live my life in a way that will in part pay my older brother back for his sacrifice. My life was saved because someone loved me enough to suffer his life to be taken.

Shouldn't we all try to live our lives in a manner pleasing to our Savior who died for us? He is our big brother and died that we might be saved and live eternally. There isn't a day that goes by that I don't thank the Lord for my brother who saved my life.

From the April 1982 New Era.

Fiction

WHO'S AFRAID OF JERRY SNOOK?

David Hammond

My name is Bruce, and I'm thirteen years old. I'm a little over five feet tall, and my voice cracks a bit when I talk. I also weigh around 170 pounds. I prefer to be thought of as pleasingly plump. At least now in junior high the school nurse doesn't storm into the class like she did at Lakewood Elementary to weigh us and shout the results across the room for the teacher to write down and everyone to hear. See, I've worked my way up in the world and now go to Chief Joseph Junior High. I'm also a member of my deacons quorum.

My quorum means a lot to me, but I don't tell people this very often. I like doing things for the quorum, like the time we went camping at Three Mile Lake and I was in charge of the food. Everything went okay except the corn bread. I thought if chocolate was good and corn bread was good, they'd be terrific together. They weren't. The quorum hasn't quite forgotten that little episode, and I've been banned for some time from all cooking. Oh, well. Then about two weeks ago the quorum president called to ask me to visit the deacon who'd moved into our ward. "Sure," I said, "what's his name?"

"Jerry Snook."

"The Jerry Snook at Chief Joseph? The Jerry Snook who is the terror of the classroom?"

"You got it."

"But I'm sure he's not a member."

"Sorry. He's just moved in from the Third Ward. He's been inactive most of his life, I guess."

I wasn't surprised. Jerry wasn't the kind of kid you'd expect to meet at church. "Do I have to do this alone?"

"Nope, we've asked Paul David to help you."

"Thanks, he'll be a big help." I mean Paul's a nice kid, but he's a little different. Most of his classes at school are for students who don't learn very fast. Still, he's a deacon, passes the sacrament with us, and participates in the lessons. And he likes to tease me about the chocolate corn bread. But for Jerry Snook I wanted somebody strong.

"And don't worry," said the quorum president. "He's already agreed to work with you."

"Wonderful," I said. And then I spoke very rapidly. "I can't go see Jerry. He hates me. It's true. Once when I said in English that I'd like to race a stock car, Jerry said real loud, 'Bruce, you could be the stock car.' Even my teacher, Mr. Robertson, laughed."

"You'll do great. Just try to see him soon. Invite him to church."

"You're sure he's a member?"

"Yeah, I'm sure. Good luck."

I hung up the phone. At first I planned to call and see when Paul would want to go out. But I decided to wait until that evening because I wanted to be sure to catch him. I told my dad about the phone call, and he said he'd be glad to help in any way. That night he helped by asking if I'd been able to reach Paul. It was a little after nine, and I didn't want to wake him. He might have been asleep. So I decided to wait until Monday. Jerry wasn't in my English class, which was a relief. And I didn't see Paul. I didn't call him that night either because I didn't want to interrupt his family home evening. My dad must have asked about ten times if I'd set up a time with Paul. Each time I promised I'd try real soon.

Tuesday I concluded it was time to give Paul a ring, but when I wasn't sure which David family to call, I thought I'd wait a day or so. When my dad found out I didn't know the correct phone number, he looked it up. "Paul's father is named Emory," he said, "and the number is 754-3961."

The next day in English I found out why I hadn't seen Jerry for a few days. Evidently, he had broken his leg playing touch football. I didn't feel very bad about it, but at least I kept my feelings to myself. I also figured I'd wait a week before visiting him so he'd have time to recuperate.

That night I was surprised when Paul called me on the phone.

"Bruce," he said slowly.

"Yes?"

"We need to see Jerry."

"I know. I've been trying to call, but your phone is always busy."

"Oh."

"Listen, he's got a broken leg, and I think we ought to let him get up and about before we go see him. Don't you agree?"

"I think we ought to go see him tomorrow."

"Well, Paul," I explained, "we can't do that because we've got to let him know we're coming, and it's too late to do that now."

"I know."

"Great. Well, I'll call him tomorrow or so and set up a day."

"I already talked to him."

"You what?"

"I called him, and he said to come on over."

"Did you say I was coming?"

"I just said that a friend and I would be over tomorrow."

"Hmm, tomorrow. You know, I'm pretty busy most days, and I've got things to do tomorrow."

"I told him tomorrow."

"Tomorrow after school?"

"Yeah."

"All right, all right. We'll go tomorrow." I paused for a second. "Hey, Paul, we don't know where he lives."

"I do. You come here, and we'll walk over together."

"Fine, fine." I told my dad that we had an appointment with Jerry, and he seemed happy.

I met Paul the next day at his house, kind of a small place with two big trees in the front. "It's not far," Paul said. "We can walk." It wasn't that close either, and I was puffing a little when we stopped in front of a brand-new house in a recently developed area.

"This is Jerry's address," Paul said. My hands felt clammy, and my stomach twisted as it always does before I have to climb a rope in PE or give a talk at church or tell my parents I failed a test. We walked up the steps, and Paul knocked on the door.

A thin, tall woman with blond hair opened the door. "Yes?" she said, looking at Paul and me as if she had caught us trying to steal the cement steps we were standing on. "Can I help you?" she added.

"We came to see Jerry," I said, "That is if he's not asleep or busy or eating or anything, because we can always come back." The woman leaned forward a bit, raised her eyebrows, and slightly pursed her lips.

Paul cleared his throat a little and said, "We're friends of his. I called yesterday."

"Oh yes, from the Church." She continued to look at me. "You know, we don't go to church very often. In fact I can't remember the last time." She looked at Paul. "Well, come in, come in." She ushered us into the living room, where we sat on some hard, wooden chairs. "Jerry, oh Jerry," she called down the hall, "the boys that called yesterday are here."

"Okay," he said, sounding bored. After a moment I could hear a thump, thump, thump that grew louder.

"He's not used to the crutches yet," his mother said. "His accident has got him down, I think."

At that moment a cast-covered leg poked through the hallway door, followed by a very red-faced Jerry who struggled with his crutches. He stared at me a moment. "What are you doing here?" he said.

"Oh," said his mother, "you really do know each other."

"A little," I said.

"Yeah, yeah. At school," Jerry added with a hint of a smirk.

"Well, I'll leave you boys for now," said his mother as she went into the kitchen.

Jerry backed up to a chair and flopped down. "So you're a Mormon," he said.

"Yes," I answered, my voice cracking a little. "Both of us are." I looked quickly at Paul.

"Yeah, we're Mormons, and we came by to invite you to come to church," he said.

Slow down, I thought. Now he'll really lay into us.

"To church?" Jerry said.

"Yes, to church. It's a good place to go, and we have a good time."

Jerry shifted his crutches to the side of his chair. "You guys want me to come to church, huh?" He glanced at me. "You want me to come even if I call you fatso and chubby?" He was smiling.

"Well," I said, my eyes a little out of focus, "sure, we both do."

"That's kind of funny, you know," Jerry said. "You guys want me to come to church. I haven't been to church for a long, long time."

"There's always a first time," Paul said.

"Yeah, there's always a first time," Jerry laughed for a second.

We were all quiet a moment.

"How'd you hurt your leg?" I asked.

"I was playing football and tripped." He looked a little embarrassed. "I feel like a jerk."

"I know what you mean," I said, and he looked at me sharply. "That is, I'm clumsy all the time."

"You mean like when you dropped your tray in the cafeteria?"

"Yeah, and it had everything on it." Even I could laugh about that incident.

"Well, that wasn't so bad. You should have seen me when I tripped. What a klutz."

"When are you coming back to school?" Paul asked.

"I don't know. Probably in a few more days. The doctor said it was a pretty bad break and that I ought to take it easy."

"That's too bad. We're working on predicate nominatives in English. Believe me, they aren't any fun. And Mr. Robertson is as hard to understand as ever."

"I'll probably have to work hard to catch up."

We all started talking about our different classes, the ones we liked and didn't like, the easy and hard ones. Jerry's mom brought out some punch. When we finished, Paul and I said that we had to go. We thanked Sister Snook for giving us something to drink. Jerry came with us to the door, not an easy feat when you're not used to crutches. "You know," he said, "nobody ever asked me to go to church. I mean just me."

"You should come."

"Maybe. Maybe I will." Jerry looked out into the street. "Is the church far?"

"No," answered Paul, "just down the street a couple of blocks. We could come by and get you."

"Give me a call, okay?"

Paul and I stepped outside. "Maybe we'll come by one of these days," Paul said.

"Sure," said Jerry. "Why don't both of you come?"

It was getting dark, so we waved good-bye and headed home.

After a moment or two Paul said, "Well, we made a start."

I left Paul at his house and walked home. When I got there, I told my dad how things had gone. He seemed pretty pleased. I felt pretty good myself. And then I had to settle down and study my predicate nominatives. They still weren't any fun.

From the June 1984 New Era.

Fiction

QUORUM
Jack Weyland

My dad said he had a big deal going that would make us
rich, but he had to leave town to go to Mexico for a few days.
He asked if we'd be all right, and we said yes. He gave me fifty
dollars for groceries, hugged us, said good-bye, threw his
sleeping bag into the '67 Ford, and left. That was four months
ago.

There are just the three of us kids. My name is Jed, and I'm
thirteen. I have a ten-year-old brother Sam. My seven-year-old
sister is named Marcie.

We've had a couple of mothers. My real mother died when
I was nine years old. She was a Mormon and had me baptized
when I was eight. Sam and I went to Primary until she died. It
was the month of March when she died. I remember how much
the wind tore at the flowers at the graveyard when we all stood
around and watched them set the casket over the place where
they had dug up the earth.

Our second mother was a woman my dad met when he was
driving a truck. Her name was Joan, and she worked in a cafe
before she met Dad. She could make real good hash browns.
I don't think she liked us children very much because Dad was
still driving and he was gone a lot. I guess we caused Joan
plenty of trouble.

Dad drove for a big moving van company. He went all over
the country. He always brought us a toy or game from wherever

he went. He went all the way to Maine once.

I'm not sure what went wrong exactly, but Dad and Joan didn't stay together long. Maybe she didn't like the responsibility of all of us kids.

Dad had to quit driving for a while. He got a job as a dispatcher for the company. I guess it didn't pay much or else he didn't like sitting at a desk. I don't blame him for that because I'd hate that too. Anyway, after a few months he quit being a dispatcher.

Then we didn't know what he was doing. He'd be gone for a few days and come back with lots of money. It was great when he came back because he'd take us out for pizza one night and to a taco place the next night. He bought us all new bicycles one time and camping and fishing gear another time.

He'd stay at home for a week or two and then be gone again. At first he paid a lady to come in and cook for us, but I told him he could save the money and I could cook as well as those women, who always wanted to feed us casseroles with plenty of noodles and cream of mushroom soup. Most women I've ever met would rather cook a casserole than just about anything.

Anyway he left for Mexico. We got along okay. We always have. But after three weeks, we were playing outside in this old, deserted car that Dad said he's going to fix up sometime. I looked around and saw one of the neighbors standing at her curtains looking at us real hard. I couldn't see how we were hurting her any because we weren't even on her property, but she looked at us for a long time.

The next day a lady came after school looking for my dad. She said she was from the county and she was a caseworker. For a while I thought she meant that she worked in a canning factory and packaged cases of food. But that's not what she did.

I couldn't figure why she came at all because all she did when she was there was sit and look. We were all watching *Gilligan's Island*. We like to do that after school, and we were having some peanut butter sandwiches and milk. She sat in front of the TV set, but she didn't watch it much. She had a clipboard, and she'd write things down. She asked if that was our supper, and Sam said yes, and she wrote that down.

We had plenty of peanut butter. When Dad was still working as a dispatcher, he heard about a truck that had been in a wreck. He bought cases of peanut butter and vegetables at a good price. Our basement was full of good deals like that.

The lady with the clipboard asked where my father was. I told her that he was away on business and that he would be back on Friday. That's what I always told everybody who asked because usually Dad did come back on Friday, and I guess he was away on business, although I didn't know what business he was in.

The lady left even before *Gilligan's Island* was over. When she stood up to go, she sort of brushed herself off like the couch was infected. I bet when she was a kid she never watched *Gilligan's Island* or ate peanut butter.

The money Dad left didn't last forever. I had to pay the light bill with part of it, and I had to get Sam a new pair of tennis shoes. It didn't take long before we were down to five dollars. Of course, we had peanut butter, but we had to buy jelly and bread, and they don't give that stuff away, you know.

I had a paper route, though, and made ten dollars a week.

One day after school I was working on an old lawn mower engine. I like to take things apart and try to figure out how they work. I don't always get them back together. The engine didn't work anyway, so I wasn't really wrecking anything.

Since we all ate around the TV, and we had a perfectly good kitchen table that we weren't using, I was using the table as a workbench.

It was about 4:30 because I remember hearing the *Brady Bunch* starting. I was working on this engine when the doorbell rang. I was afraid it was going to be that lady with the clipboard.

It was a boy about my age. He asked if I was Jed, and I said yes, and he said he was Kevin Gallagher. That didn't mean anything to me. He said he was the deacons quorum president. That made even less sense to me. To tell you the truth, he didn't look like any kind of president to me.

"So what?" I said.

I could tell he was nervous. He cleared his throat and looked like he was either going to cry or sneeze.

"I want to talk with you," he said.

"Suit yourself," I said. "Come on in the kitchen. I'm fixing a motorcycle engine."

He followed me in. I hoped he didn't know enough about engines to know that it was only a lawn mower engine and that I wasn't really fixing it. He didn't say anything about it.

He sat down on another chair after he first moved aside some wrenches.

To tell the truth, I sort of enjoyed making him nervous. I tried to look tough. I banged the wrenches together like I was a mechanic and knew what I was doing.

He sat there as stiff as a board watching me. Finally he just blurted out, "Are you a Mormon?"

"What if I am?" I said, trying to sound mean.

"You're old enough to be a deacon," he said, his eyes still moist.

"What's that?"

"We pass the sacrament and collect fast offerings."

"Why would I want to do that? I don't even know what it is."

"You could be in our Scout troop."

"What for?" I sneered. I was hoping that maybe I could get him to cry.

"We do lots of things, like go camping and fishing, and we learn to do things."

"What kind of things?" I figured I had him and that he would talk about something dumb like tying knots.

Instead he sat a minute and looked at me. Then I saw a smile come on his face, and he said "Like learning to be a mechanic."

"Oh." I tried to sound as if I wasn't interested and I already knew everything about engines and cars.

"If you come next Wednesday, we'll be starting a new course on how to fix engines. We'll have a mechanic who works at Olson's Garage showing us some things. I could come by and get you."

You see, I always thought that if I could ever get that engine to work, I'd attach it to my bicycle, but I knew I was never going to fix it the way I was going.

"I might go," I said, as coolly as I could.

He really did come by Wednesday night. I think that if I'd remembered he was coming, I might have chickened out and left the house before he got there. But I forgot until he was there; so I went with him.

When we got there, he led me right up to a man in the hall and introduced me to Bishop Townsend. The bishop reached out, shook my hand, and said he was glad I had come. Then Kevin had me meet his Scoutmaster, who was a grown man but still wore one of those green Scout uniforms. But the Scout-master wasn't so bad once you got to know him. I guess he just liked Scouting.

There were about fifteen other boys in the troop. I found out that not all of them were going to learn about engines. In fact, Kevin and I were the only ones. I've wondered since if Kevin created this whole engines mechanics course on the spot just to get me to come out. I've never asked him, but he's sneaky like that.

Anyway, we went to Olson's Garage, and this old guy, Brother Olson, showed us a lot about engines and tools. Afterwards we washed up and went back to church.

The bishop asked me if I had a good time.

"It was okay," I answered coolly. But when I thought of what I would have done at home, it was ten times better than that.

He asked if I'd come again, and I said maybe. He put his hand on my shoulder and told me that the quorum needed me. Well, it made me feel a little uncomfortable, but I couldn't help but think that he meant it.

The caseworker came by the next day. She asked where my father was, and I told her he was coming back any day. She asked me what I would think about going into a foster home until he came back, and I asked, "All of us in one home?" She said that she didn't know if she could find one home for all of us. I told her that we all stick together and that we'd rather stay home. She wrote that on the clipboard.

Then she left. I noticed that there was a small stain on the back of her dress where she had sat on an old piece of toast, but I didn't say anything. If I had, she probably would have written it down.

The next day we ran out of peanut butter. We weren't completely out of food though. We had some shortening, a package of noodles, and some tortilla flour. There was a case of green beans in the basement.

The problem was that I'd already collected from everybody on my paper route for the month, so I couldn't raise any money there.

We found that there are plenty of ways to come up with money when you think you're broke. The first thing to do is to go through all the couches and stuffed chairs and look between the frame and springs where money can drop. We found 65 cents that way. Then you can look for soda pop bottles in the basement. The grocery store will pay for them. If you check a phone booth every time you pass one, you can sometimes find a quarter in the coin return because some people don't know they get their money back if they try to make a phone call and don't get through.

Friday after school I rode my bike out to the airport, collecting empty cans along the way. The recycling center will pay almost a penny a can. At the airport there is a fountain, and sometimes people throw money in there. I've made a small rake that I can use to get the money without getting my feet wet. I got 19 pennies and 3 dimes and 4 quarters.

All in all, we got enough for another jar of peanut butter, two loaves of bread, and some pork and beans.

Saturday, while Sam and Marcie were still watching cartoons, Kevin came over and asked us to go to church with him the next day. I wasn't going to go, but he said after church his parents said it was okay to invite all of us over for supper. I said we'd go, and we did.

I don't remember much about church except in priesthood meeting Kevin ran the whole show as far as the deacons went. He got up and welcomed everybody and told them just how many he wanted to pass the sacrament. He made a point to tell the rest of them about me. He told them I was a good mechanic and that's what their quorum needed for their summer cycling trip to the mountains.

Kevin's mom really is a good cook. Sam, Marcie, and I didn't talk much, but we sure did eat.

On Monday after school the lady from the county came with a man. He had a clipboard too. He never spoke directly to us, and when he said anything to her, he talked quietly as if he were telling secrets that we weren't supposed to hear.

"Is your father back yet?" the lady asked.

"He's due back any day."

One thing about cats, they seem to know when a person doesn't like them. Our cat crawled over to the man and sat on his lap. I knew he didn't like that.

"Could we look around?" the man whispered to the lady.

"Is it all right if we look around?" the lady asked me.

"Why?" I asked her.

"We want to evaluate conditions here."

"Conditions are just fine here," I said.

Most of the time adults never listen to you. The man stood up, tried to brush off the cat hair, and went into the kitchen. She followed him.

He opened the refrigerator and shook his head. He looked in the cupboard and shook his head. He looked at the engine on the kitchen table and shook his head.

"Deplorable," he whispered to the lady.

"These poor children," she whispered back.

"I recommend foster homes as soon as possible."

"Look," I said, "my dad is coming back on Friday. We've got cases of food downstairs. We just don't keep it in the kitchen."

I ran downstairs, got the last case of green beans, and lugged it up to the kitchen. "Look, we got cases of food. If you want, I'll bring it all up." I didn't think they would go downstairs to check.

It was a lie about there being more food downstairs, and I know it's wrong to lie, but I also thought it was wrong for them to just walk in and start shaking their heads and making plans about shipping us to other homes.

"Who could we use?" the lady said to the man.

"How many children are there?" the man asked her.

"Just the three."

"The Johnson family could take one. Rosetti's can take the girl. Maybe Palmer's would take the oldest boy."

"My dad said we could definitely expect him on Friday."

The lady heard me. "The boy said his father is coming back on Friday," the lady told the man.

"I guess we could wait until Friday," the man whispered.

They left, but they sat in their car and wrote on their clipboards for five minutes in front of the house.

I knew what was coming. They were going to split us up and put us in three different homes, homes where we'd eat hot cereal for breakfast and casseroles for supper. They wouldn't know that Marcie sometimes wakes up in the middle of the night crying, but if you go in and touch her forehead for a minute, she'll fall back asleep. They wouldn't know that Sam doesn't like corn, and it doesn't matter if you say that it's good for him, he won't eat it, not plain, not creamed, and not on the cob.

There were things about them that only I knew. If we were separated, we would stop being a family. I couldn't let that happen.

I went with Kevin on Wednesday night to Scouts. They had refreshments afterwards, and I slipped two cookies in a shirt pocket to take home to Sam and Marcie.

I guess I'd told so many people that Dad was coming home Friday that I almost believed it myself. But when I woke up Friday morning, I knew we had to do something or else we'd wind up in foster homes. I got Sam and Marcie up early. While we were eating some toast and peanut butter, I turned off the TV and talked to them.

"We've got to leave town today. How would you like to go to California?"

"Why today?" Marcie asked.

"That lady who comes here, she doesn't like us living alone. She wants to make us go away and live in somebody else's home. We'd all be in different homes, and we might not see each other for a long time."

Marcie started to cry.

"Don't worry. I won't let them split us up."

We went downstairs and got our sleeping bags and packs. We put the rest of our food in my pack. Sam carried a hatchet, matches, and a flashlight in his pack along with his clothes.

We left about 9:00 in the morning. I figured that the caseworker wouldn't go to our house until after school, so I wasn't worried about hiding from them when we first started, but we wanted to get as far away as we could before night.

We took a city bus out of town as far as it went and then started walking. Sam and I could have walked faster, but Marcie slowed us down. By night we were only ten miles out of town.

Before we left, when I planned about us leaving, I pictured us in the mountains catching fish and eating berries and trapping animals for our food. Things never work out the way you picture them. Ten miles out of town we were still in the suburbs with miles and miles of shopping centers and auto dealerships. There were no trees to chop down and no berries to eat. I did find some pretty good lettuce in the garbage can behind one grocery store. It just had a couple of brown spots on it.

During the day when the wind blows, its one thing. But at night when the wind blows and it's November, that's another thing.

Finally we found a small park. Somebody had left some empty boxes that they store chicken in for picnics and some other paper in a trash container. We burned them to heat up our beans.

Then we unrolled our sleeping bags and tried to sleep. The wind was kind of spooky, and Marcie was afraid, but we had put her sleeping bag between Sam and me and told her how much fun it was to be camping out.

It was cold, and it took us a long time to get to sleep.

Sometime during the night I woke up because there was a flashlight shining in my eyes.

"What are you kids doing?" a policeman asked us.

"We're just sleeping out," I said. "We do it all the time."

"You can't sleep overnight at this park."

We put our shoes on, threw things in our packs, grabbed our sleeping bags, and walked quietly away.

He got back in his car and started to talk on his radio.

"I've just found three kids sleeping in Rock Creek Park. Have you got anything there on any runaways?"

We started to run.

He jumped out of his car and yelled after us, "Wait! I need to ask you some questions!"

Marcie fell down. I could see the man in the police car backing up so he could turn around to chase us.

I dropped my pack and sleeping bag and picked Marcie up in my arms. We ran across the street, through one yard, along an alley for a few feet, and then into another yard across the alley. We found a garage with the door open, and we ran in and quietly closed the overhead door and waited.

There was a small window on the garage door, and I looked out. The police car moved slowly past the street twice, shining his light on everything as he passed.

After half an hour he quit circling the block.

I left Sam and Marcie in the garage and went back to see if I could find our packs and sleeping bags. The policeman had taken them and was parked behind a hedge waiting for us, but I didn't let him see me.

I went back to the garage, and we stayed there for a few hours. I let Marcie and Sam sit on my coat so they wouldn't be cold sitting on the concrete. I told them I wasn't cold.

Marcie began to cry. She cried softly because she knew we'd be in trouble if the people in the house woke up. We couldn't stop her. She must have cried for half an hour.

We were beaten, and I knew it. We only had 75 cents, and we were out of food and a way to sleep. Sam and I could have gone on, but Marcie was too scared, and we wouldn't ever leave her.

It was turning gray when we left the garage and walked back to the bus stop where we had gotten off the day before. As soon as the buses began to run in the morning, we took one back to the city.

We got off the bus near our home and walked through backyards until we were close enough to see our house. I wanted to see if Dad had come home yet. He hadn't, but while we were watching, a police car drove past the house slowly.

We ran to Kevin's house, went to the back door, and knocked. Kevin opened the door and let us in.

Kevin's mom asked us if we'd like some pancakes. Sam and Marcie both said yes, and she made us some.

They didn't ask us any questions, but when Kevin's mom put some pancakes on Marcie's plate, she touched her head lightly, the way mothers do to little girls. I guess it was the wrong thing to do because Marcie broke down and started crying again.

Kevin's mom sat down and put her arms around Marcie. Marcie kept saying as she cried, "Don't let them break us apart."

Then Sam started to cry, but don't think badly of him because he's only ten years old.

We finally told Kevin and his parents what had happened. Kevin's dad called the bishop and asked him to come over.

The bishop came and took me to his office in the meetinghouse. He left Sam and Marcie at Kevin's so they could watch Saturday cartoons.

I told the bishop everything, and he promised he wouldn't let anybody split us up.

Then he got on the phone and made five or six phone calls. After he was through, he asked me if we would like to stay with Kevin's parents for a while. He said it was okay with the people from the county.

That was a month ago. My dad hasn't come back yet, but he will. One of these days he'll come back with toys and games from Mexico.

When he does, I want to tell him about the Church and about family home evenings and about the priesthood. I'm a deacon now, and Kevin and I work together in Scouting. It's not bad, Scouting I mean. You have to learn about knots, but I guess even that could be useful someday.

I've gone to priesthood meeting enough to know that what I was before I started going to church is what they call an inactive. Now I'm what they call an active. I also found out that there are more inactives than there should be. Kevin says we have to keep working to turn the inactives into actives. We talk plenty about that in priesthood meeting. I guess that's why Kevin first visited us — to turn us into actives.

You know, he really is a good president of our quorum.

From the May 1978 New Era.

BEGINNINGS

Kristy Humphreys

Fun-loving, carefree, full of a never-ending source of energy—these are common traits of a boy of twelve. One day he stands to his knees in a mud hole, rain dripping from his ears and the tip of his nose, trying to catch the prize-winning fish; and the next day, all scrubbed and with a glow of authority, he passes the sacrament.

Boys seem far from the world of marriage, government, and other grown-up things. And yet, they are on their way to eternal marriage and in their priesthood work enjoy a more perfect form of government than any country.

The Aaronic Priesthood is unlike any club. You don't buy a membership card and you're in. It is not just handed to you like a certificate. It is given to you by the laying on of hands, and you are ordained by one having authority. It is a calling from God. It is given only when a boy is worthy and is received only when given by the proper authority.

I cannot hold the priesthood, but I can help the young men of my age to honor theirs if I am modest, set a good example, and encourage them to go to their meetings and take care of their assignments. By doing this I will be helping them to keep their high goals and ideals and will be supporting them in their duties. If I can influence them for good now, together we can progress and grow. To me the Aaronic Priesthood is just the beginning of a whole new way of life.

I will live a life of cleanliness, one full of good example, because someday I want to kneel at an altar, not just any altar, but an altar at which I may take another step toward eternal life. On the other side of that altar I want someone who is clean and worthy, someone who respects his priesthood. I want him to have the best, and I want to have the best. Therefore, I hope some young man, somewhere, is thinking the same serious thoughts. By living the right way he can progress from a deacon to a teacher to a priest, and on to the higher callings of the Melchizedek Priesthood.

The Aaronic Priesthood is vital, fresh, alive—it is a beginning.

From the May 1975 New Era.

TEACHER

THE ROLE OF THE TEACHER

Elder H. Burke Peterson

As I reflected upon this subject, a story that I had recently heard by an unknown author came to my mind.

Many years ago in the foggy city of London a young man supported his widowed mother and five brothers and sisters by going to the train station at night and meeting people and then guiding them to their various destinations with his lantern through the narrow, foggy streets. On one occasion the young man was approached by a stranger who asked to be taken to a particular area of the city. It was extremely foggy, and the cobblestone streets were dangerously slippery. The boy agreed to the proposition, even though it meant placing his own life in jeopardy. The two of them started out, the boy, lantern in hand, leading the gentleman. After hours of walking they arrived at their destination. Once there the gentleman gave the young man the promised reward. The lad graciously accepted his earnings and walked briskly back to the station. He no sooner arrived at the station than several people came out of the fog, each giving the young man a like amount of money. At first the boy refused to accept the money because he felt he had not earned it. Finally one of the strangers explained: "We were all lost in this fog and had no idea where we were. Then we saw your lantern and followed your light in the distance. We only wish to repay you for guiding us to safety. Had we not followed you, we would still be lost out there in the fog."

When helping those who are lost to find their way, the ordained teacher may not be aware of the other lives he influences for good at the same time. As he magnifies his priesthood through service, he is a light for others to follow.

Many of us have had the opportunity of visiting Temple Square in Salt Lake City. On the west wall of the temple are several items of interest. One of these is a representation of the constellation Ursa Major. Its symbolism was explained by President Harold B. Lee in an address given before a mission presidents seminar on Sunday, July 2, 1961. In introducing his talk President Lee explained that during the construction of the Salt Lake Temple, the architect, Truman O. Angell, had been asked by Brigham Young to write an article for the *Millennial Star* in hopes that this would help the Saints abroad sense the need for contributions to the building project. In his article Brother Angell described the symbolism of some of the exterior parts of the temple. President Lee further described Brother Angell's article by saying:

"There are the sunstones to represent the celestial, the moonstones, and the stars. Now you have all seen those, and there are other things there; but there is one other thing that he mentioned that has particular significance that I ask you to think about here. He said that on the west end of the Temple, underneath the square of the Temple, there will be depicted the constellation which the astronomers would call Ursa Major—we call it the Dipper—where the pointers will be pointing to the North Star; that was to symbolize and to suggest to the mind 'that, through the Priesthood of God, the lost may find their way.' "

Teachers as a vital part of this priesthood force are to guide, direct, instruct, and enlighten others. As they do so, they will help the lost find their way.

Ordained teachers in the Aaronic Priesthood are assigned to perform home teaching, prepare the sacrament table, act as ushers, and to perform all of the duties of the deacon when called upon to do so. As they diligently perform these duties, they fulfill the sacred charge given them by the Lord to "watch over the church always, and be with and strengthen them" (D&C 20:53).

All of the duties of the teacher are important. In general conference in October 1970, Bishop Victor L. Brown said, "The Aaronic Priesthood is not a make-work activity designed to keep young men busy and out of trouble. It is a segment of the government of the kingdom of God on the earth. Those holding it are empowered to perform the duties that will aid the Lord in accomplishing his work and his glory" (in Conference Report, Oct. 1970, p. 125).

In the performance of home teaching, the teacher has a special opportunity to bless the lives of others and lead them to eternal life. An acquaintance of mine told me of an experience that will help to illustrate this point. "Recently," he said, "a man and his teacher-age son were assigned to our family as home teachers. We knew of the father's dedication to the gospel but did not know what to expect from his son, although the young man's appearance and conduct seemed to reflect the same dedication. During their first visit with us, I kept my eye on this young man. Though reasonably quiet, everything that he did or said brought dignity to the priesthood he bore. Soon they learned that our young son had passed away a year ago and that we were expecting another child. From that moment on they were a special part of our lives as they prayed for and encouraged us. At the conclusion of that first visit I asked the young man to offer a prayer. In his prayer he asked the Lord to sustain us in the loss of our son and to bless the child that soon would be born. He specifically prayed that my wife would have no difficulty in delivering the baby. My wife and I were overcome by the sincerity and sensitivity of this young teacher. During the days and weeks that followed these brethren inquired about us regularly (more often than once a month). Following the birth of the baby, the young man, with his father, brought a gift. As we all knelt in prayer the teacher expressed his gratitude to the Lord for the safe delivery of the child." Here is a young man who understands the importance of the assignment given him by the Lord. Other examples could be given. Home teaching is just one way in which we can use the priesthood to bless the lives of others.

A teacher has a special role in the Church. His office is a necessary appendage to the Aaronic Priesthood (see D&C 84:30). Because the office is necessary, so also is the one who fills it. The teacher must understand that just as he needs the Church, so does the Church need him.

A teacher should understand his role in the Church. Some of our number display a casual attitude toward the performance of priesthood duties. One of the reasons for this is their lack of understanding of the assignment that has been given them. We can best understand our role as we become involved in the performance of our specific duties.

I sincerely pray that the blessings of the Lord will be with each teacher that he may understand his role and fulfill it in a way that will bring honor and glory to himself and to his Father in Heaven.

From the May 1974 New Era.

HASTY

Terry Dale

After sacrament meeting the bishop called me into his office for a talk. *Here it comes,* I thought. *I'm going to be the new teachers quorum president, I'll bet.* I was filled with pride and excitement. *Wow, is the ward ever going to heap handshakes on me. Mom will be so proud!*

I sat in the big chair across from the bishop. He was a pleasant man, smiling as always but I felt that even so, this conversation was going to be an important one.

"Steve, we have an assignment for you," he said. My heart raced.

"This is a special 'good neighbor' assignment. We're concerned about Hasty McFarlan. He's a pretty sad old man, you know. He needs someone to befriend him. He's not a member of the Church, but God's love reaches to all people, and we as members of his church have the responsibility to show it. Maybe I should say we have the privilege of showing that love."

I guess I must have looked stunned.

"You know Hasty, don't you, Steve?" asked the bishop.

My memory jumped back a couple of weeks to when some friends and I had made fun of the old man by singing jingles and shouting the jokes we had made up about him.

"Yes, I know him," I said, choking down my disappointment and guilt. "He's the old hermit who lives outside of town."

"Right," said the bishop. "I would like for you to go out and visit him two or three times a week."

"Okay," was the only answer I could manage. The bishop must have detected my crestfallenness, because he leaned forward in his chair and looked at me carefully.

"Now, if this assignment will be too much, don't be afraid to say so."

I sighed. "Oh, I'll do it, sir." I said.

"Good," said the bishop with a smile, and before I could catch my breath, he went on. "You can chop wood for the fire and get him food, blankets—whatever he needs to help him feel wanted. Be a friend. Your father is aware of the assignment, and he told me he would help you. Your Heavenly Father will be prompting you, too."

"Yes, sir," I said.

I was fifteen years old then, and there were other things I would rather do—play football, hunt, fish, or just do the things my friends were doing. But I had told the bishop I would carry out the assignment, and I knew it wasn't good to go back on my word.

Hasty lived in a little log cabin at the foot of a mountain, just outside the Idaho farming community I grew up in. On the long hike to his cabin after school that first afternoon, it seemed to me that every pine along the trail whispered Hasty's loneliness.

Once a year at Christmas the old man got a free bath at the hotel, compliments of the sheriff. Probably, we all thought, it was the only bath he got all year. We used to say he looked like a pirate with that growth on the side of his head and his black eyepatch. Most of the kids and even some of the townspeople had the habit of making unkind remarks or doing something "clever" whenever Hasty was around. Would he remember me as one of the tricksters? By the time I reached the cabin, I was genuinely frightened.

I knocked. No answer. I knocked again. I knew he had to be in there. Where else could he go?

"Hasty?" My voice broke halfway through the word. I don't know how long I must have stood there before I decided to go inside. The thick oaken door creaked as I pushed it open.

"Hasty?" I called again. "Hasty, are you there?"

Hearing a rustling, I poked my head in as far as I dared and peeked around the door. It was cold in Hasty's cabin and very dark. I could just make out the figure of a man on the bed. Hasty was all slouched down, but not like he'd been asleep, or even like he'd been thinking. He looked like he was slouching because there was no reason to do anything else. I noticed that the soiled, mildewed blanket he was sitting on was more hole than blanket.

My heart was beating in my throat. I swallowed hard.

"Hasty, is there anything I can do for you?" I managed to blurt out.

I told him my name and that the bishop from the LDS church had sent me to see how he was doing and to help out. He said nothing. The silent, staring troll was freezing my nerves.

"Hasty, your fire is out."

No reply.

"Can I chop some wood?"

No reply.

I went outside, found an axe and some stacked stumps, and began chopping kindling. With every strike of the axe my brain pounded. *What am I doing out here? Why me? Why?*

"Quit grumbling," a voice inside me said. "The old man is cold and lonely, and you can help him."

I got a fire going and tried to talk to him, but after a few minutes I decided he wasn't really listening. He needed a new blanket, so I told him I would get a thick, clean, comfortable one, and the next day I did. After that I came every other day. Slowly, over the next several weeks, he began talking.

One day after we had talked some he said, "Boy, why do you come? I'm sure a kid your age can find better things to do than visit a sick old varmint like me. But I'm glad you come." And then he smiled.

At Thanksgiving I invited Hasty to our house for dinner. He didn't come, but our family took part of the dinner to him. There were tears in his eyes as he tried to thank us.

I discovered as our visits continued that Hasty had been a sheepherder. Once he had had a wife and children, but they had gotten a terrible fever and died.

Feeling in his grief that his life had been shattered, Hasty wandered the whole country as a vagabond. A diseased growth on the side of his face made one eye blind. And the teasing and practical joking had begun.

But to me the old man didn't seem as ugly and frightening anymore. In fact, after school I hurried to his cabin to help him and to listen to his stories.

When Christmas arrived, we invited him to dinner once again. This time he came, and what's more, he came in a suit, all cleaned and handsome. He looked great. A smile curved his lips. Hasty was happy because we showed him he was needed.

As we finished dinner, the old man bowed his head for a second, and then raised it and said, "You people sure are wonderful. My life has been a shambles for a long time, but the love you've shown is making me a different person. I'm very grateful."

As he said that, I could feel a little fire in my chest getting big. It felt good.

From the January-February 1981 New Era.

IT'S A SIN TO STEAL A WATERMELON

Walter L. Maughan

I considered it the better part of valor not to probe too deeply into just where the boys got the watermelon for our picnic. After all, boys would be boys, I told myself. And when they offered, what could I say? They ought to be involved somehow in the preparations. In any case, stealing a watermelon was a minor infraction. Why, we had all been involved in such things at some time or other.

I soothed my conscience with these rationalizations until I learned where they had gotten the watermelon. And then there was no help for it. Obviously it was a sin to steal a watermelon, and that would have to be the topic of our next priesthood lesson.

Not only was it a sin to steal a watermelon, but it was a greater sin to lie about it. And that was the thing that really rankled in my brain after our visit to Sister Wagner's house.

My young companion, Tom Learner, had made the appointment. And he seemed perfectly at ease as he rang the doorbell.

"Good evening, Sister Wagner," Tom's voice was sincere and friendly.

"My home teachers. Come in. I've been waiting for you."

"And how are you, Sister Wagner?" I asked.

Her answer was noncommittal. I sensed there was something she was not saying.

I discussed the message we had prepared on chastity—not

a subject that Sister Wagner needed to be greatly concerned about. Tom offered a beautiful prayer.

Then as we were preparing to leave, I said: "And how are you really, Sister Wagner? Is there something we should know about?"

With a quick glance at Tom, she said: "Come with me out back. There's something you should see."

Sister Wagner, widowed now fifteen years, was proud of her garden. Many times as we visited in her home she had taken us to look at the tomatoes and carrots and peas. And, oh yes, the one watermelon plant.

You could almost see the hunger in her eyes as she talked about eating the two large green watermelons that were growing on that vine. Tom and I had joked about them, saying that they were almost like children to her and that she probably would not have the heart to eat them when they did get ripe.

Now as we came into her backyard she pointed at the garden. She was very near to tears. "If they had just taken the watermelons, I could have accepted that. But look at my tomatoes. It looks like a herd of elephants had been running through them. All that lovely fruit spoiled! And the watermelon! Do you know what they did with the watermelon? They threw it in the street out front—smashed to pieces."

Weeping now in earnest she fled from us to the sanctuary of her house.

"Who could have done such a thing?" Tom fumed as I drove him to his house. "I'm gonna find out who it was and make him pay."

He was putting on a good act. There were real tears in his eyes, and he almost convinced me. But the circumstantial evidence was just too great. Tom was the one who had suggested that he knew where they could get a watermelon for the picnic. I felt sure that he had involved the other members of the teachers quorum in the theft.

Sick at heart, I began to prepare the lesson I would give the following Sunday. I had enjoyed working with these boys. They were good boys basically.

Where had I failed them? It was difficult for me to believe that they—Tom especially—would steal Sister Wagner's watermelons, knowing what they meant to her. Both of the melons had been taken, though only one made it to the picnic. The other one, as Sister Wagner pointed out, was dropped in the street in front of her house. Insult added to injury.

"Well, guys?"

They knew before I opened my mouth that this was not going to be the usual lesson.

"You want to tell me about it, guys?"

"What's he driving at?" Mark Fenton asked.

Tom's face was a blank.

"Hey, fellows, when you offered to get a watermelon for the picnic I assumed . . . "

Slowly the light began to dawn in Tom's eyes. I could see it expand and grow from a vague suspicion to certain knowledge.

"You, you think we took Sister Wagner's watermelon?"

"What am I supposed to think, Tom?"

Suddenly the boys were all talking at once, each one pleading innocence. I had obviously taken them by surprise. Had I really misjudged them? Or had they simply not expected to be found out?

"Okay. Okay, guys!" I raised my arms for silence. "Perhaps I did jump to conclusions. If so, I'm sorry, and I beg your forgiveness. But would you just tell me one thing? Where did you get that watermelon?"

There followed a silence as profound as the outburst of protest that had preceded it. Tom looked at Mark Fenton. Mark squirmed in his seat and glanced at Billy Chavez. Eduardo, Billy's younger brother, seemed to be profoundly interested in the pattern of the floor tiles. He studied those tiles as if he were hypnotized. The attention of the class focused finally on Eduardo, the shyest and quietest member of the group. They had chosen Eduardo as their spokesman, whether he liked it or not.

"You know something you'd like to tell me, Eduardo?"

He looked at me with something like panic in his eyes. I wanted to let him off the hook. But if the answer did not come from him, there would be no answer.

"Tell me about it, Eduardo. Where did you get the watermelon?"

Soft, like the southern breeze in September, came his voice. "From old m-m-m- . . . "

"Would you repeat that, please, Eduardo?"

"From Old Man Peters." He seemed relieved after it was out.

Relief washed over me like a mountain wind in summer. They had not stolen Sister Wagner's watermelon. They had taken one from Old Ma . . . Mr. Peters' big field. He had so many. Surely he would not miss one. Still, I had set out to make a point.

"Hey, guys. I do apologize for thinking you would do something like that to Sister Wagner, a widow with only one small plant. But you know stealing is stealing. Were you all involved in this?"

They nodded their heads affirmatively.

My plan would require only minor alteration, a change of characters. "Well, fellows, you know what I think we had better do?"

They knew all right but were hoping I would not say it.

They all agreed that, since I insisted, we would go to visit Mr. Peters later that afternoon. At the appointed time I picked each of them up and we drove out to the Peters' farm at the edge of town.

I had not talked to Bill Peters in a long time, though we went to school together some years back. He was not a member of the Church but had married into a prominent Latter-day Saint family. His children were totally inactive. I must confess that I felt somewhat ill at ease going to see him. I wondered if it was worth it for one small watermelon. But we were already committed.

He was tinkering with his tractor when we pulled into the yard. I got out of the car and approached with some trepidation.

"Hi Bill."

"Walt? Been a while." He extended his arm to shake hands and then drew it back. "Hand's covered with grease. You won't want to shake with me."

The boys were still keeping to the security of the car. I motioned them to join me.

"Looks like a delegation," Bill Peters said.

"Oh . . . uh . . . how are things going, Bill?"

"Been better. Tractor won't run. Cow got into the lucerne the other night and bloated. Still might lose her."

"I'm sorry to hear that, Bill. You have a nice looking watermelon patch."

"Hmph! Had is more like it. Kids got into the field and knocked the best melons off the vine. What they didn't ruin the cow did, on her way to the alfalfa field. Whoever got into the melon patch left her gate open."

The boys were squirming noticeably.

"Well, Bill, that . . . that was what we came to see you about."

"Figured it was when I saw you coming."

"We'd like to pay for the damage, if we could."

"Walt, I wouldn't know what to charge. Probably a couple hundred dollars all told. But, kids! They don't know what they're doing. Did you ever steal a watermelon? They think it's fun. Isn't when you're on the other side. I donno. I wouldn't feel good about taking their money. I will accept an apology."

Each of the boys in turn expressed his regret to Mr. Peters. They were deeply penitent. And none of us felt like we had really solved the problem. I did not know what more we could do.

Two weeks later I learned what kind of stuff that teachers quorum was really made of when I got a call from Bill Peters.

"Walt?"

"Yes."

"Bill Peters. I just had to tell you how much it has meant to me . . ."

My pause must have suggested to him that I did not know what he was talking about.

"Your boys," he said. "That Learner kid's a great mechanic. Got my tractor going like a charm. Brought his big brother with him, who works at the garage. And the other boys have been working around the place."

I was speechless.

We talked about it during priesthood meeting the following Sunday.

"Don't you guys know it's a sin to lie?" My voice was quavery as I said this.

"Lie?" Tom Learner's voice was indignant. "We didn't lie."

"No," Mark Fenton broke in. "We just didn't tell you everything."

"We wanted to surprise you," Eduardo spoke shyly.

Suddenly I needed a tissue. After wiping my nose, I asked: "Did you learn anything else from this experience?"

"It's a sin to steal a watermelon," Billy Chavez spoke for the group.

From the July 1983 New Era.

MY FATHER'S VOICE

Steven H. Giles

I wasn't what you would call physically intimidating. In fact, I couldn't even qualify as a ninety-eight-pound weakling. As a sophomore in high school I weighed in at a lanky ninety-five pounds. In an attempt to develop some kind of self-confidence, I had turned to wrestling.

Things were going well for me too. I'd finally broken into the varsity lineup and won a few matches when my coach decided that it would be "good experience" for me to travel with the junior varsity team for a match with a much smaller high school's varsity team.

We were all pretty cocky by the time the bus pulled up beside the gym. I mean, after all, what kind of wrestlers could such a small school have? We piled out of the bus and headed straight for the wrestling room to check our weight. The wrestling room was typical—hot and stuffy with an odd assortment of mats and weights scattered across the floor. On the wall by the scales was a chart giving their team and individual statistics. My eyes scanned down the list to find my opponent's record.

My heart fell to my stomach. He had nine wins against two losses and had placed second in a major tournament. My own record was a not-so-spectacular four and four. In addition, he led their team in almost every category—including pins.

When their team entered the room, I quickly spotted my opponent. He found me just as fast. He looked me over from head to toe. I looked him over from shoulder to shoulder. He was built like a tree stump. I was thin and lanky. In my mind I could imagine the years of bucking hay and other farm chores that had put muscles on his muscles. I looked down at my skinny arms and protruding ribs.

Right then I knew I would be victim number ten.

As the team wasted away the hours before the match, I rationalized the loss in my mind. He was obviously much stronger than I and, according to the stat sheets, also more skilled. Besides this was only a junior varsity match in a faraway town. No one would see me lose.

When we headed back to the locker rooms to dress, my heart sank again. There stood my father. He was in the area on business and had driven over to watch me wrestle. I cried inside as he introduced me to several of his friends from the area. Didn't he know I was about to be destroyed. He told me to "go get 'em." I replied with a very hollow, "Yeah, sure."

As we dressed, my mind raced. What could I do? How could he show up for this match? I resolved to not get pinned. That was respectable. It was obvious that I was outmatched. Winning was out of the question.

I halfheartedly went through the warm-up routine with the rest of the team. I could see my father up in the balcony of the small gym seated with his friends.

Mine was the first match. As I shook hands with my opponent in the center of the mat, my dad yelled out, encouraging me. How could he? Now everyone would know he was my dad. I felt embarrassed for him, knowing that my opponent was about to wipe up the mat with my skinny body.

The referee blew the whistle starting the match. The crowd erupted with cheers. In all my previous matches, once the whistle blew my mind blocked out all sounds—my coach, the cheerleaders, even the roar of the crowd. This time I could still hear my father calling, yelling, even begging me to keep going—to do my best.

I struggled, I fought. One second I was on top; the next I was flat on the mat squirming to get free. The six minutes raced by faster than ever before. My father never stopped calling to me. The final buzzer sounded. The gym fell quiet—too quiet.

I had won.

One point separated us. By listening to my father's voice, by picking it out of the crowd, I had won—something I had considered impossible just six minutes earlier. My coach called it my greatest victory. It was—not because I had won but because I knew my father's voice and I knew that he believed in me.

Today the struggle is different and the stakes are higher, but the voices from the crowd still call out.

Each day we're all engaged in a different type of struggle in an eternal arena. The voices from the crowd are still there, each telling us a different path to follow. But the key to success remains the same—learning to listen to the Father's voice.

From the September 1984 New Era.

WINNING
Keith Edwards

With a physical handicap and learning disability, Billie, at fifteen, was all but forgotten by our quorum. It was not necessary to baptize him. He had his own school to attend. With his physical handicap, Scouting had not seemed realistic. Then a new teachers quorum adviser was called. "If Billie is going to be on the rolls, then he should at least be included in the activities." Brother Wilson made the first contact, and the response was overwhelming. Sure Billie wanted to come. "No one had even thought to ask," his mother said apologetically.

Over the next few months of spring and summer Billie was at every Mutual activity, and we started to get acquainted with him. He felt like he belonged. Some of the boys didn't understand Billie and were critical of him for being clumsy and awkward, but Billie felt wanted and knew our adviser loved him.

When Billie turned sixteen, he was forgotten again, but only until some of the rest of us turned sixteen. We remembered Billie and started bringing him out; with us around again Billie felt even more accepted.

Volleyball season came. We knew we were the best team in the stake. For two years we had been knocking on the door, and this was our year. We had the veteran "senior" boys. We had the height; we had the talent. And we even had a mascot— Billie. We even let Billie play. Just hitting the ball was a major achievement, but everyone clapped and encouraged him, so

Billie really felt that he was making a contribution.

Being at each game was more important than ever to him. During the regular season, Billie might have cost the team a few points, or even one game in a series, but everyone recognized the sparkle in his eye when he played and we all felt good because of our sacrifice.

Finally the stake championship came. It was the same rivalry that had been there for the last two years. This time we would win. We had beaten them during the regular season, and we would eat them in the championship. Perhaps as an extra precaution someone "forgot" to tell Billie about the game.

Saturday afternoon at game time some of our players were overconfident and had run down to the store for some pop. The first game started without them, but the second string was good enough. Then in came the bishop with Billie. Both teams were well coached. The game was close, but we lost. We couldn't afford to hold back. We had to have the next game if we were to win two out of three.

Billie had been at the coach's side the whole first game. "Now? Should I go in now? Do you want me to play now?" His persistence was distracting. The coach spoke firmly but kindly, "Go sit down; I'll tell you when, Billie."

At the end of the first game, Billie couldn't wait any longer. Scores didn't mean anything. The only thing that was important was playing. The coach looked at Billie; for a long minute he agonized. He had always played all the boys. Would he change the rules now? Was the principle more important than the game?

This was a unique group of boys. Just weeks before, the coach had told us that sometime in his life every coach should get a chance to work with a group like ours. He felt that way we could understand principles. There wasn't any choice; he had to let Billie play.

The other team served—right to Billie. Another serve—to Billie; and another. Again and again the serve was to Billie. The other coach called time-out; he was talking to his server. Another serve—right to Billie. The score was 11 to 0; no service had been returned. Finally a service went into the net, but it was too late. The final score was 15 to 6. It was our year to win, and we lost.

The other team walked off the court with heads lowered. We were fighting back tears. We didn't understand. We went outside, and the coach tried to talk. "I thought I knew what was right." Even he was fighting for composure. "I believe it's important for everyone to play. I've always let everyone play. I hope I'm doing what's right." The bishop was there with Billie. He looked as if he wanted to talk but didn't know what to say. Finally Billie broke in and said, "Well, we won another one!"

Something happened after that. The bishop gave a lesson in priesthood meeting on winning. He said something about an inactive father going to the temple because his handicapped son was loved by our quorum. He said that was winning. Somebody said if Billie could play volleyball he could come to priesthood meeting. All of a sudden Billie was really part of us. We'd invested a volleyball championship in him, and he was important to us.

Basketball season came. Everybody knew Billie by now. Everybody knew he would be playing. The referees knew what to do when he tried to dribble. The teams made certain allowances. He was really part of things.

Stake championship again. We worked our way through the teams in the stake, and the final game was between us and— you guessed it—them.

Well, it was close the first half, but then we fell apart. The coach could see what was happening, and by the third quarter it was pretty obvious that nothing was going to work for us that night. While we were looking for some way to get even with the same guys that beat us in volleyball, something unique was happening on the basketball court.

Billie was playing. He really couldn't shoot. One arm and hand was withered, and he couldn't give much direction to the ball. But every time he got the ball, their coach yelled for someone to foul Billie. That was the end; I was fighting mad. Even the people in the crowd couldn't believe their ears. Why was our bishop smiling? Then one of their players gingerly went out and tapped Billie. One referee was so mystified by what was happening that he just stood there. In fact everybody just stood there for several silent seconds. Then the other referee blew his whistle, and when he did everyone understood. Billie got to shoot a foul shot. In fact, he got to shoot two foul shots (intentional foul), and when he missed those, one of the boys on the other team was standing with his foot over the line and Billie got to shoot again, in fact several more.

The crowd was clapping and cheering for Billie; we were cheering for him, but so was the other team. Was this really losing? Everyone was pulling together. No one seemed to care what the score was; everyone was helping Billie. Both teams were helping and cheering and pulling for Billie.

Billie shot a lot of free throws that night. We all cheered; we laughed a little; and Billie went home the star of the evening. Who won? They did, we did, and the stake did.

We found out that when we forget ourselves and our selfish goals, scores aren't as important as the individual; and we found out that we all care about the same thing. Those guys on that other team aren't so bad. The referees are really human. And losing a game isn't the end of the world, not when you're winning.

We went on that year to play in the Explorer Olympics. We played team sports in volleyball and basketball, and we won some and we lost some. But our investment in Billie was there, and we taught some other teams—or Billie taught some other teams—that winning only matters if you're building your own stature or, as our bishop says, "if you're developing character." And I guess that's what we learned from Billie—character.

Our bishop said that Billie is here to teach us. We're all watching him a little more closely to see what other lessons we might learn from him.

From the May 1983 New Era.

PRIEST

THE ROLE OF THE PRIEST

Elder Victor L. Brown

From the time I was a small boy in western Canada I have loved horses. Until I was about fifteen years old, my father always made sure that my brothers and I had a horse. Over the years we owned several. Some were sleepy ponies. One or two were spirited and well bred. From the time I was a young priest until about age fifty, circumstances made it impossible for me to have a horse even though I still loved them. During the past few years I have owned a well-bred mare.

Although my schedule limits my contact with these horses, they have been a source of happiness to me; but more importantly, they have exposed me to some very valuable lessons that have helped me learn to honor my priesthood, both as an Aaronic Priesthood youth and as an adult. I should like to share some of them with you.

One day my father brought home a beautiful, spirited thoroughbred. She had been fully trained as a polo pony. She happened to be about half a hand too small to qualify for the buyer of the rest of the string, so my father bought her for us. This was one of the most exciting gifts I had ever had. Here was a prize any boy would be thrilled with. She could take off like a jack rabbit. She could stop on a dime, back up almost on a run, do anything any other horse could do, and do it better. She was a thoroughbred; yet, she lacked one thing. Almost every time I got on her, she ran away with me. Perhaps it was my fault, but she simply would not accept authority. She would take the bit in her teeth and take off, paying no attention to where I wanted to go. She was a rebel. All her training and talent were lost because she was headstrong and resented authority. We had named her Lady, but it was not long before we stopped calling her Lady and finally gave her away.

Clipper was a beautiful sorrel. He was half thoroughbred and a well-trained cow pony. When we turned him loose in the field after a hard day's ride, he would kick up his heels and run and buck just like a frisky colt. One day I was trying to drive our cow home but to no avail; so I roped her, wrapping the rope around the horn of my saddle. Just as she came to the end of the rope, the cinch on my saddle broke, and both the saddle and I ended up on the ground under Clipper. He had been running hard and was excited, yet he stopped instantly and did not move a muscle until I was out of danger.

Now to Katie, the horse I acquired a few years ago. She has a very prestigious pedigree. Each of her parents was a champion. Katie is a beautiful chestnut. She is intelligent and holds her head high. Her first foal has won many ribbons in competition in harness and in the three-gaited class.

When we first got Katie she was in poor condition. She had been mistreated and not fed properly. But I felt that with proper care she would respond, and she did. She is the best bred and most handsome horse I have ever owned. She would be a real champion except for one thing — she has never learned proper discipline. Her early training was poor. She is fun to ride for a short while. She prances, holds her head high, lifts her feet, and looks wonderful; but the moment she is startled or comes upon an unknown object, she loses her head. One day she was startled by a dog. She reared up on her hind legs, causing her to fall over on her back and on me, injuring my leg. She then struggled to her feet and ran like a frightened deer. With all her beauty and intelligence, she is now out to pasture.

Suzzie was Katie's foal. She is about six years old now. She is as beautiful as her mother. Suzzie received some training about three years ago. Since then her training has been used very seldom. She has almost retrogressed to the level of her performance prior to her first handling. Had she been worked with regularly, she would now be a delight to ride.

In no way do I equate the intelligence of a fine young man with that of a horse. However, I do think there is much wisdom in the saying "He has good common *horse sense.*" You priests in the Aaronic Priesthood are of a royal generation. You are sons of God with great power and unlimited potential. You have been in training for the past five or six years in preparation for the greatest honor and responsibility that comes to man, and that is the Melchizedek Priesthood—the power to act in the name of God and have your actions ratified in the heavens. In the process of your training, you have been taught by presiding officers, particularly your bishop, who is president of your quorum. He has given you instruction with regard to the sacrament service and baptism and your responsibility for home teaching and now is giving you instruction in leadership in the Young Men program. He has taught you how your appearance and cleanliness both externally and internally are so important if you are to be a proper example to others.

As you preside at the sacrament table, you are making it possible for members of the Church to renew their covenants with the Lord. This you do through the power of your priesthood. As you perform a baptism, you exercise the same priesthood John the Baptist held as he baptized the Savior in the River Jordan. And as you "visit the house of each member, and exhort them to pray vocally and in secret and attend to all family duties" (D&C 20:47), you are again exercising your priesthood as a home teacher.

If you have learned these lessons well, you will have found the fulfillment that can come only from service to your fellowmen, which, of course, is service to your God. These principles can help you overcome the power of Satan, which in one form is rebellion. You will find a harmony with those in authority, and you will in very deed become a true thoroughbred prepared to serve as a missionary, be married in the temple, and assume responsibilities of great leadership in the Church.

Along with your bishop I have great faith in each of you and know that as you fully honor your priesthood you will participate in the building of the kingdom of God on earth in your own significant way. I pray the Lord's blessing on you as you continue your quest for excellence.

From the May 1974 New Era.

YOUR TESTIMONY

Elder Robert L. Simpson

Jim had just turned eighteen. He was sitting across from a General Authority of the Church, obviously nervous, filled with frustration, and showing a lot of animosity. His request was forthright, simple, and came out like he couldn't wait to say it.

"I want to be excommunicated from the Church—today!"

"How long have you been a member?"

"About three years," came the answer.

"Why do you make such a request?"

"Because I have lost my free agency. I like to smoke, and the Church is depriving me of my free agency to live the way I want to live."

Jim failed to recognize that his most important exercise of free agency occurred when he decided to be baptized and to live in accordance with gospel standards.

Jim had obviously acquired associations with peers outside the Church who had gradually dulled the spiritual sensitivity and uplift that he had felt at the time of his baptismal commitment.

He was no longer a free young man. He had fallen prey to one of the adversary's many ploys and deceptions which deceives the very elect at times and entices people away from the truth. Jim complained that the Church was depriving him of his freedom. But in actuality, it is the truth of the gospel that makes us free (see John 8:32). We all have a great need to be free.

It was quite late. The missionaries had just finished their scripture reading and turned out the light as an anxious knock at the door broke the silence. Elder Franklin swung the door open to find Steve, one of their fine young converts of nine months, standing there without his usual smile and holding a rolled up paper in his hand.

"Elder Franklin," he said, "I have come to give you my priesthood certificate of ordination. Please hold it for me until I can work out a problem. I don't feel worthy of the priesthood right now, but I know I will be back to pick it up real soon."

As it turned out, what Steve did was not necessary—except perhaps for his own peace of mind until he was able to sort things out to his own satisfaction. But peace of mind is the key. He had no peace while a conflict existed with his priesthood calling. We all need peace—peace of mind.

Sue was extremely quiet as the family drove home from fast and testimony meeting. So quiet, in fact, that her father sought an opportunity within the hour to talk with her alone. To make a long story short, Sue was laboring under the illusion that she really didn't have a testimony of the gospel. Two or three members that day had expressed "sure knowledge" that the gospel was true, and in tears Sue said, "Daddy, I can't say that I know it's true, and that troubles me."

Sue's dad was patient and understanding, for his mind was remembering clearly his teenage years of developing testimony.

"Sue," he asked, "why do you pay tithing?"

"Because I know it's a commandment from the Lord," she replied promptly.

Sue's dad then led her mind through a quick rerun of some basic principles, including the Word of Wisdom, the law of the fast, partaking of the sacrament, high moral standards, and prayer. To each of these Sue was able to relate positively and promptly. Soon she smiled at her father and said, "Gee, Daddy, I guess I do have a testimony of sorts about everything you mentioned. I suppose I could bear my testimony about the things I understand."

And that's the way it is with all of us. Sue had certainly felt a lack of security in this Church, which she loved, but not after her father had proven to her that she was on schedule with a developing testimony about many truths. Real security comes with a developing testimony. Hopefully, we'll be spending much of our time here in mortality developing our testimony, improving our testimony, and sensing the wonderful security that comes with each new truth riveted securely in its place. We all have an urgent need for security.

From the beginning people have sought to be free. People through the ages have felt the extreme need for security. However hardened and perverse they may have become, people really and truly, way down deep, would like to have peace of mind.

Aren't you grateful that we as Latter-day Saints are the custodians of the greatest flood of truth that has ever descended upon the earth in any age? A primary aim is to stand from our vantage point and share freely this revealed truth, for the Savior has declared that "the truth shall make you free" (John 8:32). You and I need to listen to a living prophet and abide by his teachings.

Peace seems to be an important object in this world and always has been. Peace on earth was one of the key messages declared by heavenly hosts heralding the birth of the Savior. Yet during three recent wars, hundreds of Latter-day Saint young men found themselves "dug in" while mortar shells, bombs, and rockets threatened their very lives from all sides. Agnostics claim that Christianity has failed because in these last 2,000 years there has been no peace, only war and contention among men.

The scriptures tell us that this mortal probation will be plagued with contention, discord, wars, and rumors of wars, especially in the last days. The Savior knew this as he declared, "Peace I leave with you, my peace I give unto you: not as the world giveth, give I unto you" (John 14:27). He was undoubtedly speaking of "the peace of God, which passeth all understanding" (Philip. 4:7)—peace of mind—the peace that comes with personal testimony. And that's why there can be peace in foxholes with fire power descending from all directions. Peace has always been the companion of him who can say under all conditions and circumstances, "I know that my Redeemer liveth." Peace of mind accompanies every developing testimony. But beware lest that growing testimony linger too long on a dormant plateau. More people in this world need to find the kind of peace spoken of by the Master.

Aren't you grateful that real security comes in knowing that God the Father and his Son really appeared in a sacred grove in this period of the world's history, or in knowing that the heavens have been opened and that priesthood authority—the right to act in His sacred name—has been restored? Aren't you grateful to know for a surety that baptism by immersion was accomplished by the Savior as he set the example for all mankind? He sought one having authority, John the Baptist. They both went to a place where there was "much water" (John 3:23), and the scriptures record that the Savior came "up out of the water" (Mark 1:10). That is the kind of security that the world needs to know about.

Aren't you thankful that peace of mind is a personal thing, based on a personal relationship with Heavenly Father and his beloved Son? *What is a developing testimony other than a developing understanding of truth and an ever increasing capability to love the Savior?* "If ye love me," he said, "keep my commandments" (John 14:15). In so doing, there comes peace that you and I should be anxious to share liberally and freely.

Oh, youth of Zion! Stand firm in these things above all else. The world would give anything for what is within your grasp. At your fingertips is freedom from the threatening shackles of the adversary, by finding truth and living it. You have the beginning of a firm foundation and the total security that comes through a developing divine partnership. Yours can be the peace of mind that is guaranteed to all who would come to know him.

From the August 1984 New Era.

A QUESTION OF HONOR

Alma J. Yates

Trevor Sims turned the volume up on the radio as he turned down Cherry Drive and accelerated for home. Now that Brad was gone and he was alone, he needed a distraction to ward off his nagging conscience. Earlier, while Brad had been with him, everything had been so funny. They had laughed and made light of their evening, but now as Trevor drove home there were mirthless regrets. The humor had long since dissipated; only the bitter realization remained.

He pulled into the driveway and parked the family car. He saw a lamp burning in the living room. He squirmed uneasily in his seat and suddenly felt a queasy reluctance to go inside. Did his parents know, he wondered. Several excuses flashed through his mind, excuses which had seemed so valid earlier and now seemed empty and trite.

Whistling quietly in an attempt to allay his own anxiety and appear casual, he strode across the lawn, leaped up the steps, and pushed open the front door. His father sat in his easy chair reading his scriptures, something he did early every morning — or when he was troubled. Trevor glanced at his watch and then at his father, who peered over the top of his reading glasses.

"You're up late," Trevor remarked with a forced smile. "Checking up on me?"

His father closed his scriptures and pulled the glasses from his nose and smiled. "How did it go?" he inquired cheerfully. "Did you have a good time?"

Trevor avoided his father's eyes, sank onto the sofa, and grabbed a magazine. "Oh, it was all right," he remarked, thumbing through the magazine. He could feel his father's gaze upon him, and he sensed a warm guilt redden his cheeks. That was what happened when a boy's father was the bishop, he thought. Bishops seemed to have that uncanny ability to look right inside you and know what secret thoughts you harbored there. Of course, Trevor's father had been like that even before he was made bishop, but Trevor felt it more nowadays, especially tonight.

"How did you like Michelle?"

Trevor shrugged indifferently, trying to avoid an untruth. The thought of telling a lie to his father had always been repugnant to him, and yet right now he didn't feel capable of telling the truth. The truth shamed him. He groped for a noncommittal answer, one that would not plunge him into a lie but which would circumvent the truth just enough. "Oh, Michelle's all right—for a sophomore. She's not the greatest girl in the world, but she's—well, I don't know how to describe her. I'm not planning to go out with her again if that's what you mean."

"She called tonight," his father said simply. It was a mere statement, and yet the words hit Trevor like a powerful hammer. His stomach knotted, and he felt the blood creep up his neck and flood his cheeks.

"What'd she want?" Trevor asked, attempting to sound disinterested.

His father set his scriptures to one side and sat up, his forearms on his knees and his head and shoulders leaning forward. "She called about an hour after you left. She was wondering where you were." The room was silent. Trevor suddenly wished that the evening had been different. "I told her that there was no need to worry, that I was sure you would be there soon. I said you might have had car trouble or that Brad might have been late." He chuckled. "I think she was worried you might stand her up. I told her not to worry though. I told her you weren't that kind of a boy."

"I guess we did have a little trouble," Trevor explained, fidgeting and thumbing rapidly through the magazine and then closing it without having read a single word. "Well, I better get to bed. That welfare project at the stake farm is tomorrow morning, isn't it?"

"Six o'clock."

Trevor stood and stared down the hall to his bedroom.

"Trevor," his father called after him. Trevor stopped without turning around. "Did Michelle have a good time?"

"How should I know? I didn't ask her." There was a sharp edge in his voice, one he rarely used with his father, and he had not meant to use it then. It just slipped out.

"I was just wondering," his father replied, no rebuke in his voice. "These girls' choice dances are always hard on a girl. They take them so seriously. It would be a shame if they worked and waited for weeks and then didn't have a good time. I always worry about the girls."

"Well, I didn't ask her," Trevor mumbled. "I guess I'm going to bed."

Inside his bedroom, Trevor sat on the edge of his bed without getting undressed. He grabbed his pillow and flung it angrily across the room. If his father had accused him, he wouldn't feel so bad now, but he had merely asked, not out of suspicion but out of concern. Trevor slammed his fist hard into the mattress. If he had just not listened to Brad's proddings, Trevor thought. If he had just said no rather than having toyed with the idea as he had done and finally succumbed to Brad's coaxing.

For almost fifteen minutes he sat on the edge of his bed, his conscience refusing him any peace. Finally he stood, opened his door, and returned to the living room, where his father still sat reading.

"You might as well know it. I didn't pick her up," Trevor blurted out, as though he were challenging his father to chastize him, ground him, anything to appease his conscience. His father looked up but didn't answer. "I didn't want to go," Trevor argued. "Brad didn't want to go either, so we stood them up. They shouldn't have asked us. I hate these girls' choice dances. You're always stuck with someone you'd never pick in a thousand years."

"Like the girls are most of the time?" his father asked with a wan smile.

"That's different. It's the boy's job to ask. If the girl doesn't want to go she doesn't have to."

His father took a deep breath and stared down at his opened scriptures. "All she has to do is stand the guy up. Is that what you mean?" he asked softly.

Trevor licked his lips. "No, she can, well, she can tell him when he calls."

His father set his scriptures aside. "Couldn't you have done the same thing with Michelle?" he asked in the same quiet tone.

"She had no business asking me," he retorted, searching for some justification. "Nobody told her I wanted to go. She hardly knows me. And she's as homely as a mud fence—glasses, braces, and she's only a sophomore."

"Does any of that give you the right to hurt another person, to break a promise?"

"I didn't promise."

"Didn't you accept the date?"

"But I didn't promise. I didn't promise I would go."

His father took a deep breath. "Trevor, a person does not have to preface everything with 'I promise' to make a promise. When a person says he will be at a certain place at a certain time, he has made a promise. If he fails to appear, unless there is a very good reason, he has broken his promise. Maybe not in a court of law, but he's broken a promise in the Lord's court—in the long run that's the only one that counts."

Trevor looked at his father and then at the floor. He pushed his hands into his pockets and shifted his weight from one foot to the other. He knew his father was right. His own argument was just a front, a hasty attempt to clothe a wrong in respectability. "Okay, I should have gone," Trevor admitted begrudgingly. "I'm sorry."

"I told Michelle I was sure you would come. I told her that you weren't the kind of young man to let a person down, that you were true to your word."

"Look, Dad, I said I was sorry."

His father nodded his head. "I know you're sorry, Trevor, but I don't deserve the apology. I wasn't stood up. I guess I'm a little disappointed, but I'll get over that because I know you. I know that you probably didn't do this maliciously. I accept that. I doubt you'll ever do anything like this again. But, Trevor, someone has been wronged. Someone has been hurt."

"Oh, it's no big deal. It was just a dumb dance. There will be another one sometime. She can ask someone then—someone who wants to go."

His father shook his head ruefully. "It's more than a dumb dance, Trevor. It's your word and Michelle's feelings, her entire evening and probably more than that."

"Come on, you're making a big deal out of it. If I got stood up, I wouldn't lose sleep over it."

"You're not a girl. It's different with a boy." He paused. "When did Michelle ask you?"

"Two or three weeks ago."

"Do you ask girls out that much in advance?" Trevor shook his head. "No, because it's no big deal, as you said. But with a girl like Michelle it is a big deal. She's planned this. Maybe it's her first date. She probably made a dress just for tonight. She's probably planned this thing for weeks, even before she asked you. She probably fixed her hair special. She has probably talked this over with her friends. She's proud and honored that you accepted, and all her friends will know that. They will also know you didn't show up.

"With a boy it's different. He takes a shower, combs his hair wet, puts on the same suit, walks out the door, and doesn't really think about the evening until it's started. If he's ever stood up, he might let off a little steam, his friends might kid him in the locker room, and then he forgets the whole thing, unless it's to joke about it later."

Trevor's father bowed his head and was silent for a moment, and then he continued, his voice soft: "This wasn't just a dumb dance for Michelle. I know. You have two older sisters. I've watched them get ready. I've watched them wait and fret, and I've seen them when they were brokenhearted." He looked up at Trevor and asked, "How would you feel if someone did to your sister Susan what you have done to Michelle?"

"She doesn't even date."

"She will." He paused. "How would you feel?" he persisted. "Would it be no big deal? It would be a big deal to me."

Trevor knew he was wrong. He had known it all during the movie he and Brad had decided to see. "All right," he conceded, "I'll apologize Monday. Will that make you happy?"

His father leaned back in his chair. "Trevor, you didn't stand me up. Michelle is the one you need to consider, her and Brother and Sister Stewart. They've all been anxious. Are you going to make them wait and wonder until Monday?"

"You don't expect me to go there tonight?"

"You told her you would be there."

"But, Dad, it's almost midnight. They'll all be in bed."

"I doubt it. With her hair fixed, her new dress ready, her parents and family expectant, excited to greet this young man their daughter and sister has asked out. No, she won't be in bed. She won't be ready to go to a dance, but sleep won't come easy tonight, not for any of them. Do you think it's fair for you to go to bed and sleep and leave them hanging, not knowing why?"

"But, Dad, not tonight," Trevor pleaded.

His father took a deep breath and began to speak: "I knew a boy once who stood up a girl. He was a senior, like you. She was a junior. It was a hayride for girls' glee club. She asked him to go, and he accepted—reluctantly.

"First of all he felt quiet superiority to the girl. He was an athlete and rather popular. She was shy and a little homely. Her complexion wasn't good. She wore braces and glasses. For two weeks he thought of how he might get out of his commitment. Well, the night of the hayride he had a bit of a cold. Nothing serious. He had gone to school, but he rationalized that he was too sick to go on a hayride.

"Half an hour before the date he called her and cancelled. He tried to sound sick, but she wasn't fooled, even though she did accept his excuse graciously. He went to bed to at least give his excuse a semblance of truth. But he didn't sleep. He had lied, and he knew it; he knew that there were some girls who could have asked him and he would have made the date regardless.

"At eleven o'clock that evening he got out of bed and went over and apologized to her. I know for a fact that it was the most difficult thing he had ever done up to that point. I also know for a fact that he never regretted doing it."

The room was silent. Trevor stared at the floor and stuffed his hands into his pockets. He wished he could relive the evening. He was trapped. He could go to his room and climb into bed, but sleep would elude him. His father was right, and yet he hesitated, his cowardice standing obstinately in his way. "So you think I should go tonight, is that it?"

"Trevor, I've always had a lot of faith in you. I still do. I can't make decisions for you. You have to decide. But whatever you do, make sure that you're the one who decides. Don't go because you think I want you to, because when you look back on this moment, you'll want to look back on something that you decided and did."

The minutes ticked away. Trevor stood before his father, not debating his course of action. That was settled, even though he had not yet verbalized his resolve. The pause was an attempt to build his courage. It had taken no courage to leave Michelle waiting. It would require a great deal of courage to face her now.

"Can I take the car?" he asked in a whisper. His father nodded. Slowly he turned and walked to the front door, his stomach churning, his mouth dry and his hands slightly shaking.

On the way over to the Stewarts' home Trevor hoped that the

house would be dark, everyone in bed, giving him an excuse to postpone the confrontation. He groped for an apology, something that would lessen the ignominy of his tardiness, but his nervousness prevented him from organizing anything coherent.

Finally he was there. One light burned in an upstairs window. He knew if he lingered in the car for just a moment he would lose courage and never go through with it. He stepped from the car, and before he fully realized it he was at the door ringing the bell. His heart was pounding, and his breathing was deep and almost painful. All the while he hoped that no one would come, that the upstairs light would flick off and leave him in the black stillness.

Soon he heard footsteps; then the porch light flipped on and the front door opened a few inches. Mr. Stewart stood there, still dressed, no sign that he had been in bed that evening. There was no smile or greeting, just a curt "Yes?" which came out more as a challenge than a question.

"Is Michelle up?" Trevor ventured, his voice cracking slightly. Mr. Stewart stared at him for a moment without answering and then nodded his head. "Can I speak with her?"

Mr. Stewart looked at his watch and glanced back into the house. "It's a little late," he answered shortly.

"I know, but I think I need to talk to her—if I could."

Mr. Stewart took a deep breath and said gruffly, "I'll go check." He was about to leave Trevor standing on the porch, but he reconsidered and invited him in by opening the door a little wider and motioning with his head.

For almost five minutes Trevor waited, and then Mrs. Stewart stepped in and said, "She'll be here in just a second."

"Oh, Mrs. Stewart," Trevor called out, "could you and your husband come in too."

The three of them were soon standing there. The two parents entered somberly and Michelle followed timidly, avoiding his eyes, but even in the shadows of the dimly lighted room Trevor could see she had been crying. She wore her dress, and although her hair was a little messed up, it was apparent that it had been fixed earlier.

"I want you to know," Trevor began shakily licking his lips and shuffling his feet, "that I have no excuse for tonight. I'm sorry. I'm not here to tell you why I didn't come, because that doesn't make any difference now." He paused and sucked in a breath of air. "I'm here to tell you that . . . well, that I'm sorry.

I know that doesn't fix things up, but about all I can do tonight is tell you that I realize how wrong and cruel I was. I guess I didn't think about that earlier, or I wouldn't have done it."

"It's all right," Michelle mumbled, looking at the floor.

There was a long awkward silence, and then Trevor continued: "There is something I would like to do though. I know you think I'm a real—well, I don't know what—and I wouldn't blame you if you wanted to avoid me and never see me again, but I would like to show you that tonight isn't a good example of what I'm like. I think I'm better than that, and I'd like to prove it to you. I would like to take you someplace, someplace nice, and show you that I'm a lot better than what you probably think I am. I know I don't have any right to ask you to go, but I'd like you to give me another chance. I won't blame you if you don't want to. I'll understand if you say no."

Trevor couldn't remember the rest. He didn't know how he finally ended up in the car, but he was there and he felt good. He was even looking forward to the next weekend, and he was determined that it would be a memorable one.

When he arrived home, the light in the living room was still on, and as he came in the door he found his father still reading. At least the scriptures were still on his lap, but Trevor guessed that his father had not read much. The misty blur in his father's eyes was evidence of that. His father looked up as he came in.

"Well," Trevor announced humbly, "I did it."

His father smiled. "I knew you would. I'm proud of you. It took a lot of courage, but you'll be a better person for having gone."

They were both pensively silent for several minutes, each content to be alone with his own thoughts. Finally his father sighed. "You know that boy I told you about earlier?" he asked. Trevor nodded. "Well, he forgot about that girl—for a little while anyway." He smiled. "After his mission and two years of college, he saw her again. She had changed." He chuckled, leaned back, and stared up at the ceiling. "She had shed her braces and glasses, and her complexion had improved. She wasn't the same girl. In fact, he didn't even recognize her at first. He wanted to ask her out, but he didn't dare. He was afraid she would remember. She was in demand then. Finally he built up his courage and asked her out, hoping all along that she wouldn't remember that night five years earlier. She did though, but she accepted anyway. She told him later—after they were engaged to be married—that it was because he had gone to her home that evening and apologized that she accepted his date later. She said she knew how much courage it must have taken and she always respected him for that."

Trevor smiled and glanced slyly at his father. "I think I know that boy."

"Which boy?" his father asked with mock surprise.

"The boy you're talking about."

His father smiled, pushed himself to his feet, stepped up to his son, and put his arm over his shoulders. "Yes," he said with a smile, "I think you do know him. I believe he married your mother."

From the May 1983 New Era.

THRILLS

Terry Nofsinger

Young people seem to like thrills. It may be riding a roller coaster, climbing a mountain, surfing, riding a bucking horse, or scuba diving. I like thrills too. I would like to share with you two of the thrills I have enjoyed in my life.

Several years ago I had the opportunity of playing quarterback in the National Football League. Over a seven-year period I played for the Pittsburgh Steelers, the St. Louis Cardinals, and the Atlanta Falcons.

The first of the two thrills took place one day when I was playing with the Steelers against the Philadelphia Eagles. On the first play of the game from scrimmage, I faked to the halfback and dropped back into the pocket. I threw a long pass down the sideline, and my receiver, who was racing down the sideline as fast as he could go, reached out with one hand, caught the ball, pulled it in, and went all the way for a touchdown.

That touchdown pass was a great thrill for me. It was really exciting with 80,000 people cheering. Not many people will have that particular thrill during their lifetime.

The second thrill happened after I retired from professional football. A young man became interested in the gospel through some discussions we had. I invited him to my home. He brought his girl friend with him, and the full-time missionaries taught him the gospel. They were converted. I had the opportunity of baptizing these two young people. A year later they came to Salt Lake City, and I had the privilege of going through the Salt Lake Temple with them when they were sealed for time and eternity.

The experience of seeing those beautiful young people accept the gospel and be united forever was a great thrill. It was a different kind of thrill than the touchdown pass. There were only a few people present in the "sacred silence," but it was still very exciting.

When I compare the thrill of the touchdown pass with the thrill of those baptisms, there is absolutely no comparison. The baptisms were far more exciting! That may sound phony at first, because "now we see through a glass, darkly" (1 Cor. 13:12), but I testify that the greatest thrills in this life come from serving the Lord.

It's perfectly logical when we think about it. Who is going to remember that touchdown pass? Just two people—myself and the fellow who caught the ball. No one else will feel the impact or even remember the play. Just try to remember who played in the Super Bowl two years ago.

In contrast, contemplate all those who will remember the baptisms: this young couple's children, grandchildren, and many generations to come, not to mention those this couple have brought into the Church.

At the day of judgment, the books will be opened, and those baptisms will be noted. We will be able to see that record, and angels will look upon it. Many will feel the impact of this thrill throughout eternity. "And now, if your joy will be great with one soul that you have brought unto me into the kingdom of my Father, how great will be your joy if you should bring many souls unto me!" (D&C 18:16). And while few of us may experience the thrill of a touchdown pass, every young man and woman in the Church can know the greater thrill of sharing the gospel!

There are many exciting thrills in life, but we will enjoy the greatest of them through the gospel by learning and growing, by teaching, by sharing, by serving as a friend and a missionary. If we can learn to love the things that God loves, we will comprehend the true meaning of life, and we will seek after the joy of the gospel with all our heart, might, mind, and strength.

From the November 1982 New Era.

HUNTING ACCIDENT

Kent Jackson

High overhead a flock of ducks locked their wings and dropped down toward the reservoir. It was early morning, and it was duck hunting season. I was in the bulrushes on one side of the reservoir, and two of my friends, Rick and Kinnley, were on the opposite side. The ducks circled the pond several times and then whistled down directly in front of the place Rick and Kinnley were hiding.

I heard three shots. The ducks came up fast. I heard a fourth shot. I remember wondering about it because the ducks were out of range when I heard it. The ducks flew out across the valley and began circling over some small ponds.

Kinnley ran out of the place they'd been hiding and yelled, "Skip, come here." I knew there would be more ducks coming, and I didn't want to move. Before I could answer, Kinnley ran back into the bulrushes. He came out again in just a few seconds.

"Skip, hurry!" he yelled.

I ran over as fast as I could so that I would be in position if more ducks flew over. When I reached Kinnley I knew something was wrong. His face was white.

"My gun jammed," he stammered. "Rick's been hurt."

We ran into the bulrushes, and there I saw one of the most gruesome sights in my life. Here was one of my best friends writhing in pain from a shotgun blast in the side. Rick was moaning. "Help me, you guys, you've got to help me."

I knew that we had to stop the bleeding immediately and then we'd have to get help. The nearest town was several miles away. We bound the wound up with Kinnley's shirt. It didn't help much. Rick was dying. Kinnley and I both knew there wasn't much time left. Our truck was on a road about two miles away. We knew we couldn't carry Rick to it, and getting help would take time, maybe too much time. While we were trying to decide what to do, Kinnley said, "Skip, let's give him a blessing."

We knelt by his side and placed our hands on his head.

"You go first," Kinnley said.

With the power of the Aaronic Priesthood, I asked that the bleeding would stop, that Rick would be relieved of pain, and that he would survive the accident. I also prayed that Kinnley and I would be able to think clearly in getting Rick to a hospital.

When we finished our prayers and took our hands off his head, a feeling of peace replaced the panic we'd felt before. I told Kinnley to run and get the truck. I took off my coat and overalls to keep Rick warm. I put a coat under his head and carefully laid him on the side opposite of the wound. He was getting weaker. I tried to assure him that it wasn't all that bad and that he was going to be all right.

Never in all of my life had I felt so totally helpless, my friend in so much pain, dying, pleading for me not to let him die, blood soaking through the shirt we'd bound the wound in. I pleaded with the Lord to please, please let him live.

Kinnley came back with the truck. His face was even whiter than it had been before. We decided we couldn't risk moving Rick. I left in the truck to call an ambulance. The road was rough, and it seemed like it took me hours to reach the town. I knew that every second counted.

I went into a cafe and said there'd been an accident. I went to a pay phone, the closest telephone, and called the hospital. I told them to send the ambulance to the junction in the road that turned off the main highway to the reservoir.

Several men in the cafe offered to help. We drove to the junction and waited. I can't remember waiting for anything in my life as long as I waited for that ambulance. It actually took only three minutes from the time I called until the ambulance reached the junction.

The ambulance started following me to the reservoir, but the road was too rough. The ambulance crew loaded equipment into the back of my truck and we started again. It seemed like hours since I'd left Rick and Kinnley, and I didn't know what I would find.

When we reached them, Kinnley stood up.

"Skip, look at Rick."

Rick was breathing easier, and it appeared that the pain had subsided. The ambulance crew went to work. They put a pair of pressurized pants on Rick and pumped them up. In just minutes his blood pressure was close to normal, and in about a half hour he had stabilized enough to be moved. The ambulance crew and several of the men from the cafe lifted Rick onto the back of the truck and started for the ambulance.

I stayed behind to get our coats and guns. I sat there by myself for a while and said a prayer thanking my Father in Heaven. A week later Kinnley and I visited Rick in the hospital. He was sitting up in bed playing an electric basketball game, smiling. The experience strengthened my testimony of the priesthood. I knew the blessing we gave to Rick had helped save his life and had helped Kinnley and me make the right decisions.

From the November 1984 New Era.

STRIKE
THE STEEL

B. Lloyd Poelman

"I want you to knock all the cement off these steel posts," the boss said as he handed me the sledgehammer and stood back to watch me begin. Anxious to impress him with my eagerness for the task, I planted my feet in a wide stance, raised the sledgehammer high above my head, and brought it down hard on the barrel-sized keg of cement caked on the first leg of the extracted guardrail.

Six . . . seven . . . eight solid follow-up strokes to the same spot, but all I could feel was the stunning reverberation up the handle of the sledgehammer. Not a single chip of the hard cement seemed to yield under the blows. After resting the hammerhead on the ground for a moment and rubbing my right shoulder, again I raised the hammer high above my head and repeated the effort, but with no better result.

I felt a little embarrassed as the boss watched a minute longer. Then, starting to walk toward the tool shop, he said, "I'll get you something that may help."

As I had arrived for work that morning wearing ankle-high work shoes, with cowhide gloves dangling from the back pocket of my denims, I had wondered, as I had on the two previous mornings, if this would be my last day on the job. I hoped not. With only three months before I would enter the mission home, I needed every penny I could earn to help cover my mission expenses, for the first few months at least.

Dad said no sacrifice by the family would be too great for the privilege of supporting me in the mission field, and he meant it. He knew what that kind of sacrifice was. I remember how the family had spread margarine on the bread and then scraped most of it off again while my older brother Ron was in the mission field. I also sensed Dad's special gratitude when occasionally I was able to spare a few dollars of the earnings from my part-time job to add to what was sent to Ron.

Yes, I knew it would mean sacrifice, gladly offered. I also knew I had to do all I could.

I took a firmer grasp on the handle, holding it a little lower this time to get a better weight advantage from the heavy steel head. Several more strokes, and now I could feel myself becoming angry. How could I strike any harder? Why didn't the cement break?

"I hope he doesn't get back before I've shown some kind of progress," I said to myself, glancing toward the tool shop.

When I had told the boss on Monday morning that I had quit school to work for a few months so I could go on a mission, I had hoped he would be kind of proud of me. Instead he had said, "Why do you want to waste your time like that?" Ever since then he had seemed bent on going out of his way to make snide comments about the Church and other crude remarks that, I suspected, were designed to shock me. But he was the boss and the one who would let me stay or let me go.

I had been much more comfortable last week when I first got this job and was helping Bert Godfrey lay a brick wall to replace an old wooden one that had burned down. How could I help but like that leather-faced but kindhearted man who had served three missions, two of them building missions.

The company had hired me for ten days, mostly to help build that wall. But Bert and I had worked so well together that we had finished it in a week. He didn't seem to mind that I was a bit clumsy and lacked experience. He knew I was trying and he knew why. He just kept talking to me about serving the Lord.

Bert hadn't told me that the real boss was on vacation, and it had come as a surprise when I showed up for work the next Monday morning. So far, though, my strategy seemed to be working. Although I was earning more than I had ever earned before, I figured that if I worked so hard that I was worth still more than they were paying me, maybe the boss would feel he just couldn't afford to let me go.

I looked again at the long I-beam rail with thirteen steel legs extending from it like a giant comb with most of its teeth missing.

It had long ago served as a bumper guard, preventing cars in the parking lot from hitting the adjacent building. It had been installed by digging thirteen large holes in the ground in a straight line, spaced at eight-foot intervals. A steel post was cemented into each hole, and the connecting bumper rail welded to each post. Recently the entire rail had been removed by having two large Hysters extract the whole thing in one piece, and it was lying in the driveway with each post encased in a barrel-sized cement block.

As I heard boots scuff the loose gravel on the asphalt pavement leading from the tool shop, I let loose a wild flurry of blows. I was glad that a few beads of sweat had formed on my forehead. "Here, try this," the boss said as he handed me a heavier sledgehammer. That wasn't quite the kind of help I had in mind.

I smiled as I traded him the smaller hammer, but I could tell that he sensed it wasn't a completely honest smile. He watched me for a few minutes more, and then without further comment, turned away to supervise the crew working on the remodeling project in the steel fabrication plant.

"The only difference between the hammers is that this one is heavier and harder to lift," I grumbled silently as the steel head collided with the stonehard cement. Finally one small chunk broke off. After several more strokes my arms started to ache, but the cement still remained intact.

At this rate I knew it would take me three days to complete the job. I also knew that if I didn't show substantial progress by noon, I'd be out of a job and back standing in the labor lines at the Employment Security Office taking any kind of work available. Three days of that had made me especially anxious to keep this job.

Besides, it was 1954, and thousands of striking workers with families to feed were looking for short-term, full-time employment. How was a twenty-year-old youth going to compete with them for the few jobs available?

It took only a few more hard but unsuccessful strokes to persuade me that I had reached my limit and that it was time for me to treat the problem as one needing more strength and wisdom than I possessed.

Resting the heavy hammer on the ground and trying to compose my anger and frustration, I felt the need and desire to discuss the problem with the Lord. Without either kneeling or closing my eyes, I started praying aloud to the Lord and explaining the task I faced. In a conversational but sincere way I reminded him that I wasn't asking for the money so I could buy a yellow convertible. He had called me on a mission, and I knew he wanted me to go. This job had already been an answer to my prayers, but I needed to keep it. I didn't expect him to send a host of angels from heaven with sledgehammers, but I knew he could help me.

Never in my life has a prayer been answered more immediately or clearly. Suddenly my mind was filled with a thought so lucid and strong that my heart started pounding. It was a simple solution, as I later considered it. To brighter or more experienced minds it might have occurred earlier, but to me it came as a direct answer to my prayer.

The compelling instruction said to me, "Instead of striking the cement, strike the steel."

Still not fathoming exactly why, I raised the hammer and brought it crashing down five or six times on the steel post right next to the cement. As a large section of the cement cracked into big chunks and fell off, I realized that the blows to the steel had started a series of strong vibrations that were transmitted all along the steel shaft.

I quickly forgot the weight of the hammer. With new energy I struck the steel again and again, then moved on to the next post, amazed at the magnification of my efforts as the steel vibrated and the cement cracked.

Less than two hours later I had removed the cement from all thirteen posts and stacked the large chunks in a pile. With the sledgehammer on my shoulder and a prayer of gratitude in my heart, I went to find the boss.

"I'll need some help moving the railing out of the driveway," I said, trying to conceal the excitement I felt inside. Thinking I was giving up on the project, he motioned me to follow him to the parking lot.

As we rounded the corner of the building and he saw the railing and the pile of cement, he stopped quite suddenly. His eyes blinked and opened wide. His chin started to drop a bit. For a full minute he stood silently, looking first at the railing, then at the cement. After a moment more he turned, motioned me to follow him again, and said, "Come on, I'll give you another job."

Nothing more was said about the incident, but the following morning when I arrived for work, he simply said, "Lloyd, you're welcome to stay on as long as you like."

I worked there for nearly three months before entering the

mission home. He then let me come back to work again for another ten days until I departed with my group for the mission field. Never after that memorable morning did he, in my presence, make a disparaging remark about the Church or my plans to serve a mission.

Many times since that day the Lord has helped me strike the steel instead of the cement in solving other problems. But as I departed for the mission field in late November 1954, I knew that I was called of the Lord. I knew that he was listening to my prayers. And I knew for myself that he would give no commandment save he would prepare a way for it to be accomplished.

From the January-February 1981 New Era.

RONNY'S BUDDY

D. Brent Collette

Ronny was not just shy; he was downright backward. As a seventeen-year-old high school senior, Ronny had never really had a close friend or done anything that included other people. He was famous for his shyness. He never said anything to anybody, not even a teacher. One look at him told you a great deal of the story—inferiority complex. He slumped over as if to hide his face and seemed to be always looking at his feet. He always sat in the back of the class and would never participate. He was such a novelty, it became kind of a school joke.

One thing you could say about him—he came by his complex honestly. His parents were the same way. People right next door went months without even seeing them. Ronny's father was a night custodian for a small business building. He left for work late at night, worked alone, and came home just as others were getting up. Neighbors used to joke that they never ate because they were afraid to go to the store—afraid someone might talk to them.

It was because of Ronny's shyness that I was so astonished when he started coming to my Sunday School class. He was a member of the Church. I vaguely remembered when a relative from out of town came to baptize him. Ronny was fourteen then, and so shy that a special baptismal service had to be arranged. Just Ronny, his uncle, the bishop, and the missionaries. It must have about killed him being the center of attention.

His attendance in my class was the result of the personal efforts of a classmember, Brandon Craig, who had recently befriended Ronny. Boy, if there had ever been a mismatch, this was it. Brandon was "Mr. Social." A good head taller than Ronny, he was indisputedly the number one star of our high school athletics program. Brandon was involved in everything and successful at everything. You had to smile whenever you looked at him. He was just a neat kid.

Well, Brandon took to little Ronny like glue. Class was obviously painful for Ronny, but Brandon protected him like the king's guard. I played a low profile—no questions, just a quick smile and once a pat on the back. Time seemed to be helping, but I often wondered if Brandon and company (the rest of the class certainly played it right) would ever be able to break the ice. That's why I was so shocked when Brian, the class president, stood before our Sunday School class one Sunday afternoon and boldly announced that Ronny would offer the opening prayer.

There was a moment of hesitation; then Ronny slowly came to his feet. Still looking at his shoes, he walked to the front of the room. He folded his arms (his head was already bowed). The class was frozen solid. I thought to myself, "If he does it, we'll all be translated."

Then almost at a whisper I heard, "Our Father in Heaven, thank you for our Sunday School class." Then silence—long, loud silence! I could feel poor Ronny suffering. Then came a few sniffles and a muffled sob.

"Oh, no," I thought, "I should be up front where I can help."

I hurt for him; we all did. I opened an eye and looked up to make my way to Ronny. But Brandon beat me to it. With an eye still open I watched six-foot-four Brandon put his arm around his friend, bend down and put his chin on Ronny's shoulder, then whisper the words of a short, sweet prayer. Ronny struggled for composure, then repeated the prayer.

But when the prayer was over, Ronny kept his head bowed and added: "Thank you for Brandon, amen." He then turned and looked up at his big buddy and said clear enough for all to hear, "I love you, Brandon."

Brandon, who still had his arm around him, responded, "I love you too, Ronny. And that was fun."

And it was, for all of us.

From the May 1983 New Era.

PREPARATION FOR POWER

Robert Marcum

It was a warm but very pleasant summer evening. Bob and his friend Phil had just finished eating their charcoal-broiled hamburgers. As Bob leaned back in his lawn chair, he saw a sudden commotion in a neighbor's yard a few houses away. At first he ignored it, but as the noise increased it bothered him more.

Almost at the same moment he and Phil stood up to get a better view. As they did, they heard a yell for help.

Before they realized it, they were running at full speed down the block toward the neighbor's home. As they ran into the carport, their neighbor Ken came from his back door with the smallest of his eight children in his arms. In his hand he held a bottle of consecrated oil.

"Phil," he said, "I want you to anoint my son. Quickly! He has been run over by a car!" There was not panic in his voice, but Bob could feel the tension and emotion of the situation. Phil quickly took the oil and anointed the small, gasping child. Then they all laid their hands on the child's head, and Ken gave an immediate blessing and command for his son to live long enough to get medical help.

As the sealing was closed Bob opened his eyes and felt a calm feeling, interrupted only momentarily by the sight of the baby, now turning a bluish color from lack of oxygen.

Ken and his wife left the family in the care of Bob and Phil and rushed to a nearby hospital. Although it was normally a thirty-minute drive through traffic and intermittent lights, they arrived in fifteen.

After one of the older children explained what had happened, Phil called the hospital so they would be prepared to properly treat the baby. Then they all sat down to wait for information of the baby's welfare.

After what seemed like an eternity the phone rang, startling them all into action. Phil was the first to reach the receiver; the rest listened intently for any clue about how things were at the hospital.

"Hello! Yes, Ken, this is Phil. How's the baby?" Silence — then, "That's great," Phil sighed.

The house was joyous as the children jumped on each other, yelling and screaming.

"Quiet!" Phil yelled. "There's more. Go ahead Ken. I couldn't hear that last part."

Everyone reacted to the tension in Phil's voice, and it became deathly silent as they listened to catch what else had been said.

When Phil hung up the phone he turned to the family with a show of concern on his face, but slowly a smile replaced it.

"Your little brother is okay," he said, "but they must keep him there for a while to make sure nothing goes wrong. His lungs were crushed, and the doctors don't know how he even survived, but he'll be fine after a lot of good care."

The house was a turmoil again as the children expressed their pent up emotions and love for their baby brother. As Bob watched he realized he had witnessed a miracle. The doctors couldn't explain it, but they hadn't been there when Ken blessed his tiny son. They hadn't felt the warmth of the Spirit whisper to him that the baby would be okay.

Ken's first thoughts had been to use his priesthood to bless his child, and he had been prepared to do so. Emergencies will come into all of our lives, some very similar to this one, and we must be prepared for them. How can all priesthood bearers develop the faith and power in the priesthood that Ken had when he most needed it?

As a fast express train rounded a bend, the engineer suddenly saw, a short distance ahead, a freight wreck on the track next to his own. Two cars had buckled over and lay in the path of his train. There was no time to slow up; there was not a moment to think. In a flash the engineer pulled the throttle wide open and yelled to the fireman to duck down low. The terrific impetus of the express knocked the wrecked cars from the track in splintered debris, and the train was brought to a stop a half mile on the other side of the wreck.

As the passengers crowded about the engineer, one asked how, in such a moment of crisis, he could think quickly enough to make and to act upon the only decision that could have saved his train from wrecking. He replied, "I did not have to think. I had often thought of such a possibility, and I made up my mind ten years ago just what I would do if such a situation arose. When it did come I acted instinctively."

We can be prepared for many of life's emergencies in the same way the engineer was. We can plan ahead, think things through thoroughly, and make decisions that will give us strength to use the priesthood when it is most needed. Elder Marvin J. Ashton has explained what we must do *now* to properly prepare:

"As holders of the holy priesthood, we must be true to correct principles. We have a responsibility to continue faithfully in being true to the gospel. We cannot take a rest or vacation from these principles. We will be judged according to our ability and strength in continuing in his word" ("To Teach, to Testify, to Be True," in *Priesthood*, Salt Lake City: Deseret Book Co., 1981, p. 99).

One can begin to imagine what might have happened had the engineer not decided ahead how to act or if Ken had "taken a vacation" from honoring his priesthood.

Each office in the Aaronic Priesthood has designated responsibilities. If a young man seldom performs these tasks, he is merely "taking a vacation." If he decides in his youth to put off magnifying his priesthood—if he refuses to serve others by performing such duties as administering the sacrament, home teaching, visiting the sick and the needy, working on the welfare farm, and keeping the commandments—how can he be ready to perform the proper functions of the Melchizedek Priesthood?

President Kimball has said: "It is most appropriate for Aaronic Priesthood youth . . . to quietly, and with determination, set some serious personal goals in which they will seek to improve by selecting certain things that they will accomplish within a specified period of time. Even if the priesthood holders of our Heavenly Father are headed in the right direction, if they are men without momentum they will have too little influence. You are the leaven on which the world depends; you must use your powers to stop a drifting and aimless world.

"We hope we can help our young men and young women to realize . . . that they need to make certain decisions only once. We can push some things away from us once and have done with them. We can make a single decision about certain things that we will incorporate in our lives and then make them ours— without having to brood and redecide a hundred times what it is we will do and what we will not do. Indecision and discouragement are climates in which the adversary likes to function, for he can inflict so many casualties among mankind in those settings" ("The Privilege of Holding the Priesthood," in *Priesthood*, Salt Lake City: Deseret Book Co., 1981, pp. 5–6).

He is counseling youth to prepare as the engineer did, so when the emergency comes they are ready. Because of a previous decision by the engineer, the momentum of the train saved the lives of hundreds of people. So it is with bearers of the priesthood: decisions must be made early in life, so the momentum we gain through time will carry us through the emergencies life offers: decisions about studying the scriptures, praying morning and night, resisting challenges to break the Word of Wisdom and lower our moral standards. If you make those kinds of decisions *now*, while young, you will be prepared for all the emergencies that come your way.

About two years ago my son and I watched a nationally televised basketball game. The BYU Cougars had just won the Western Athletic Conference championship and were being congratulated by sports broadcasters. As they talked with different members of the team, a sophomore by the name of Devin Durrant was interviewed about his plans for the coming year. My son, who was ten at the time and very sports minded, watched intently as Devin told of his decision to fill a mission first and play basketball later. At that moment I was thankful for a young man who knew the importance of making decisions before the moment to decide. Like the engineer, he knew what to do when the time came. My son and I saw a young man who had set goals, made decisions, and been true to those decisions.

As Elder Ashton said: "Being true involves much sacrifice— much heart, might, mind and strength. If we are obedient to priesthood leaders, priesthood principles, and priesthood responsibilities, we will find ourselves being obedient and true to ourselves. . . .

"The Savior has taught us the rewards for being true. He has said: 'Verily, verily, I say unto you, If a man keep my saying, he shall never see death.' (John 8:51.) Each of us must resolve to be true, to be faithful, to be worthy of the trust placed in us. God will help us. We and God are a majority, and we can be victorious in all of life's challenges if we will continue in his strength" ("To Teach, to Testify, to Be True," p. 100).

God has not sent us here to be losers, but to be winners. He has not chosen us to fail, but to succeed. If we are to do so, however, we must decide while we are young that we will be faithful in our priesthood responsibilities. In his poem "Maud Miller," John Greenleaf Whittier wrote, "Of all sad words of tongue or pen, the saddest are these: 'It might have been!' " (stanza 53).

No such words should be a part of our report to the Savior about our lives and the use of the gifts of the priesthood with which we have been entrusted. With proper preparation now, the priesthood can lead us to power and the ability to help ourselves and serve others as the emergencies of life present themselves.

From the May 1983 New Era.